CW00420722

ISO 14000 and ISO 9000

ISO 14000 and ISO 9000

BRIAN ROTHERY

Gower

Published by
Gower Publishing Limited
Gower House
Croft Road
Aldershot
Hampshire GU11 3HR
England

Gower
Old Post Road
Brookfield
Vermont 05036
USA

British Library Cataloguing in Publication data

Rothery, Brian
ISO 14000 and ISO 9000
I. Title
658.562

ISBN 0–566–07648–9

Library of Congress Cataloging-in-Publication Data
Rothery, Brian.
ISO 14000 and ISO 9000 / Brian Rothery.
p. cm.
Includes index.
ISBN 0-566-07648-9
1. ISO 9000 Series Standards. 2. Environmental protection--Standards. I. Title.
TS156.6.R68 1995
658.5'62--dc20 95-22035
CIP

Edited, designed and typeset from author's disk by Bill Ireson, Norwich.
Printed in Great Britain by the University Press, Cambridge.

Contents

Preface

In 1991 I had the good fortune to publish a book about the phenomenally successful ISO 9000 standard. The book was simply titled *ISO 9000*, and appears to have been the first book anywhere on the subject. Lifted by the huge interest worldwide in the standard, the book became a bestseller and went into ten overseas translations and other editions. It also sold worldwide in the English language edition.

I followed this in 1993 with the first book on the new environmental management standard, *BS 7750*. This was chosen by the British Standards Institute as a 'BSI bestseller' in 1994, and became a best-selling business book in the United Kingdom.

By 1995 many books about ISO 9000 had been published. There were also 1994 Phase One revisions to the standard, and Phase Two revisions being planned, while the ISO technical committee TC 207 was developing the ISO environmental management standard, ISO 14000, apparently based on BS 7750.

Many companies were concerned that neither ISO 9000 nor ISO 14000 dealt adequately with staff health and safety, and the chemical industry in particular was advocating a SHEM approach – safety, health and environmental management. Quality in the ISO 9000 sense had become routine in the chemical industry. The standard which really mattered was the environmental management standard, as it could control traditional environmental issues, staff health and safety, public/process safety and product safety. In ISO 9000, ISO 14000 and BS 7750 and other national standards, staff health and safety was grudgingly admitted as an issue which could be included under the environmental management standard if a company wished to do so.

By 1994 I had come to the conclusion that the task facing companies was to anticipate both the Phase Two changes to ISO 9000 and the final form of ISO 14000, and, whether or not either standard accommodated the health and safety issue, build it into a system, because industry had to control it, particularly as it attracted potential corporate and personal liability, should a charge of negligence arise.

There was a solution on hand. It was the chemical industry's Responsible Care Programme (RCP), which in its wisdom took quality for granted and treated all internal and external safety issues as environmental issues.

This book, therefore, does not attempt to predict the detailed contents of the coming revised ISO 9000 and final ISO 14000 standards, but suggests a management system which should meet their requirements as it is *issue based*, not document based, although documents are included. Fortunately, at the time of writing the main discussion and committee documents, or first drafts of ISO 14000, are available and they contain no surprises, so some confidence can be expressed about the ISO 14000 material, particularly as it also reflects the requirements of BS 7750.

There is a backlash against the so-called 'ISO 9000 certification' process which uses checklists of documents to please inspectors, rather than implementing real quality improvement schemes. The advice contained in this book is that you should implement a good, comprehensive system and tell the certifying inspector that you are interested in having the system which manages your *significant issues* audited, not a set of bureaucratic documents.

In early 1995 a very important document, *Environmental Accreditation Criteria* was published in the United Kingdom by the NACCB (National Accreditation Council for Certification Bodies).

This document lays down criteria both for certification bodies and what they should look for in their assessments of companies seeking certification to BS 7750 or registration to the European Union's Eco Management and Audit Scheme Regulation, known as EMAS. It clearly reflects the backlash against using checklists for ISO 9000 certifications and insists that real, significant issues be addressed. It also sensibly declares that the company can develop its own management systems and fit the modules together as required.

The NACCB document may be the first benchmark for the rules deciding what constitutes an adequate environmental management system for which certification is being sought. I have checked it against the relevant text in this book and included some information from it. I have also been fortunate to be able to work and co-operate both with some of the first companies to implement BS 7750/ISO 9000 systems and with the UK/Swiss certification agency SGS.

What follows now is a work which attempts to explain the two standards and supply an actual generic system for their adoption and management. It is hoped that the reader can customize this to his or her particular application requirements.

1

How to use this book

The purpose of this book is to help the reader to implement a full ISO 9000/ISO 14000 management system, which also takes account of staff health and safety, process, public and product or service safety. While the ISO 9000 section deals with the quality management issue, part of it also shows how the chemical industry uses ISO 9000 to manage environment and health and safety issues in some plants. The ISO 14000 section covers general environmental, staff health and safety, process and public safety, and product safety issues. ISO 9000 can also be used to give protection against product liability and to ensure the meeting of the requirements of consumer information and misleading advertising legislation.

Both the ISO 9000 and the ISO 14000 sections can be used independently. This has become important for companies implementing environmental management systems, as the accreditation agencies, such as the NACCB (which accredits certification agencies in the UK), expect that new environmental management systems will be implemented separately, not as add-ons to ISO 9000, although the two can be combined later. A company may not yet have completed an ISO 9000 management system and will need to do so if it is being demanded by customers. Another company may have implemented an ISO 9000 system and be facing the implementation of an ISO 14000 system and needs to know how it should fit in with ISO 9000. There will be some companies, because of the environmental implications of their work, wanting to implement ISO 14000 before ISO 9000; and there will be some capable people who will want to implement a fully integrated ISO 9000/ISO 14000 system. In the last case steps must be taken to ensure that there is a stand-alone ISO 14000 system, which can have certain administrative parts, such as document control cross-referenced to ISO 9000, for the purposes of first-time assessment by certification inspectors.

The 1994 Phase One revisions to ISO 9000 have been used throughout and the author has tried to anticipate the coming Phase Two revisions. If the system proposed here is as comprehensive as the author believes it to be, it should satisfy both standards, as it tries to deal with significant issues and their effects. Indeed, all the significant issues dealt with here are covered by legislation, and therefore amenable to management through the employment of standards. The only other major element of a company's operations also legislated for and not included here is finance. The reason for its exclusion is that it has had its own body of knowledge and set of precise standards for about 200 years. In the near future, however, it may become integrated with quality and environment into a total management standard.

As far as the many other issues or functions of management are concerned – planning, marketing, sales, public relations, and so on – these can all be carried out in an incompetent way, should a company choose to do so, and not infringe either the law directly or cause immediate de-listing from customers' vendor approved lists. However, such a choice may result in de-listing eventually, whereas the market demands of ISO 9000, as distinct from product liability demands, make it virtually compulsory. In this context, the reader may find it interesting that all of these key issues, which are covered by legislation, product integrity, description and safety, environmental probity of materials and process, staff safety, and public safety, are now covered by management standards. This is a good reminder that the way to meet legal requirements in industry is to employ standards, whether these apply to the product, process or management system.

There is a certain amount of commentary in this book, but as many other books (including those by this author) give plenty of background and commentary on the standards, the emphasis here is to advise the reader on their implementation. The procedure chosen is, then, one of describing, and providing examples of, key documentation. Were it possible, full samples of all documents would be provided, but that would involve hundreds of pages, many of them partially or mostly blank, as a company must fill in its own operating activities in many of the procedures needed. Such full documentation is already available for two categories of companies: general manufacturers and chemical companies. (See the two previous works by this author, *Keypac 2000* for general manufacturers and *Chempac 2000* for chemical companies, which are boxed sets of six manuals each, available from the publishers of this book, Gower.)

As full documentation cannot be provided here, samples of each major document or register are given, together with the contents list of each major document. The contents list is fundamental to both standards. For example, contents lists in the Quality Manual (see Appendix 1) and Environmental Management Manual (see Appendix 2) give not just contents of a document, but describe all of the necessary system elements.

The practical way for companies to implement either of the two standards is to take the contents list of the manual in question and use it as an overall master list of the elements needed and as a basis for also both planning and constructing the documentation. The documentation in turn tells us what is needed on the shop floor, so that, once we get it on paper, we at least know what needs to be done at shop floor level.

There are purists who criticize this approach, some even involved with the technical committees which have developed the standards. There is also criticism aimed at companies taking this approach simply to achieve certification, where there is more interest in being certified than in operating quality or environmentally driven companies. However correct this point of view, the fault is not with the companies, most of whom have to implement the standards to survive in business, but with repressive certification schemes which are forcing them to use such checklists to ensure certification.

Apart from the certification motivation, the checklist is an ideal approach to the management of any project and the author could neither implement the standards nor write books about them without using it.

To summarize: use the proposed documentation, in particular the contents lists of key documents, as your overall guide and use the detailed samples of documents for the detailed system. If you wish to make things easier, obtain a complete sample of documentation (from a source such as Gower) and customize it for your own operations in the blank spaces provided.

2

The market and industrial environment

ISO – The International Organization for Standardization

The International Organization for Standardization (ISO), based in Geneva, is a worldwide federation of national standards bodies from some 90 countries, one from each country. It is a non-governmental organization established in 1947. The main outcome of ISO's work is in international agreements which are published as international standards. Its national members provide their country's share of financial support for the central operations of ISO, through payment of membership dues.

ISO's sister body, also based in Geneva, the International Electrotechnical Commission (IEC), deals with electrical and electrotechnical standards, leaving all other product and management standards to ISO. On the world stage, ISO is what in the European theatre is CEN; CEN is the European Committee for Standardization. It represents all of the European national standards bodies and advises the EU on matters of standardization. The national standards bodies of all the European countries are members of both CEN and ISO, while those of more than 70 other countries are also members of ISO. World trade agreements depend upon the harmonized standards produced by these bodies through ISO and the IEC. Through CEN, and its European members, the 'technical barriers to trade' have been removed to create a truly single market in the EU.

All the important standards development work of ISO is carried out by technical committees, known as 'TCs', for example 'TC 207'. Each major new standard becomes the responsibility of one of the national standards bodies that make up the ISO membership. For example, the Standards Council of Canada (SCA) is the member body holding the secretariat for TC 207, the committee overseeing other sub-committees developing ISO 14000, the environmental management standard.

What is driving the standards?

Both ISO 9000 and ISO 14000 are part of a world trend, which some biologists or physicists might call a dominant tendency. The spread of the standards is a process which is facilitating its own growth, almost biological, and the growth has been described as a 'cascade effect'. The particular mechanism causing this biological type growth is the customer-buyer interface. As sophisticated buyers demand the standards from their immediate suppliers, those suppliers in turn pass on the demand to their suppliers, so that it cascades through the supply chain.

A very good example is a large international user of print and packaging for products sold worldwide, software perhaps with manuals, packaged in cartons, which demands that its print and packaging suppliers supply materials with environmental probity. The suppliers pass the demand back to the paper and board mills, which in turn insist that the timber comes from managed forests. The mechanism for monitoring this up the supply stream is an ISO 9000/ISO 14000 system in each facility from print and packaging company to forest.

If the process is a biological or social development, then it may be a kind of necessity, an adaptive response to pressing industrial and social needs, driven in the first instance by the energy and environmental crises, and now by the demands of an increasingly regulated world for greater accountability. The process may be no less than a manifestation of the world's growing need for accuracy and order, and it may not be an exaggeration to say that even the concepts of truth and honesty are incorporated into the new regime, legislated for and subjected to third party verification.

The new management standards are built upon such elements as *exact specifications*, *precise procedures and instructions*, processes, the *minimization* of waste, *fitness* for purpose, *consistency* of output, honest and *correct* descriptions, performance *evaluation*, the *health and safety* of workers and the *community*, and the protection of the *environment*.

Growth of the standards

The British Standards Institute (BSI) virtually invented the standards in the late 1970s, by producing the world's first quality management standard, BS 5750. The UK still leads the world in the numbers of companies certified to BS 5750/ISO 9000. BS 5750 has since become ISO 9000.

The European Commission started the worldwide spread of ISO 9000 when in 1987 it instructed CEN, the European standards body, to adopt ISO 9000 as the harmonized quality management standard for the coming internal, or 'single' market of the European Union (EU).

As European companies adopted ISO 9000, so did US companies in Europe, and soon it was spreading to sister and parent companies in the US and worldwide. Europe did not rest with a harmonized quality management standard but moved quickly to harmonized testing and certification schemes.

In 1992 the BSI produced a second pioneering management standard when it published BS 7750, the world's first environmental management standard. Just as BS 5750 was the model for ISO 9000 so BS 7750 became the model for ISO 14000. BS 7750 also anticipated EMAS, the EU Eco management and audit scheme regulation, known as the EMAS regulation.

At the time of writing, ISO 9000 is still the standard sweeping the world, while BS 7750, and a few other national environmental management standards, such as the French AFNOR standard, are being adopted by large or sophisticated companies. The signs are, however, that the environmental management standard will embrace quality and have a growth as spectacular as ISO 9000, and perhaps even more so. A number of people, including those in the powerful chemical industry, want to see one standard with environment, health and safety as the dominant elements, where quality will be a minimum requirement.

In 1994 a Mobil survey, carried out through its international network of offices for ISO and published in ISO's *ISO 9000 News*, revealed that the number of ISO 9000 certifications was approaching 100,000. Between the end of September 1993 and the end of June 1994, the number rose from 46,546 to 70,517, a phenomenal growth which appears to be approaching 100 per cent per annum. In descending order of magnitude the UK had the greatest number of certifications followed by Europe in general, North America, Australia and New Zealand, the Far East and the rest of world. The figures are changing continuously as growth in countries which have recently adopted the standard tends to be higher than in the more mature countries.

The Mobil survey also revealed that companies had been certified in 76 countries, and the most rapid growth, around 150 per cent, was in the US and Japan. Singapore and Malaysia were experiencing 100 per cent growth, with Germany not far behind. Even such 'mature' countries as the UK were experiencing certification growth rates in excess of 50 per cent, which was remarkable seeing that the UK had over 40,000 sites certified. Not revealed in the survey is the number of countries with certification bodies; however, it did reveal that 12 certification bodies had issued 71.6 per cent of all certificates, and were working in at least 12 countries, which suggests that the majority of countries do not have accredited certification bodies, which puts their companies at a considerable disadvantage.

The survey's instigator, Dr John Symonds, when asked about a guess for the year 2000, replied, 'Any bets on a million – or will it be two million?' It seems certain that adoption of the standard is expanding at almost exponential rates worldwide.

Independently, the author compared Ireland – which, with the UK, led with certifications in the early stages – with Malaysia. Ireland, because of an aggressive government programme to ensure the competitiveness of Irish industry in the single market of the EU, had up to 1994 the second largest number of companies certified to ISO 9000 after the UK. With a figure of over 1,000, but with only 3,000 to 4,000 companies as potential candidates compared with hundreds of thousands in larger economies such as those of the US, France and Germany, it is only a matter of time before Ireland slips down the league of number of companies certified. A second important reason for Ireland's early lead was the high number of resident US manufacturers who quickly adopted the standard and passed it on to local suppliers. Malaysia followed with almost the same pattern. The Malaysian government was also determined that the country would not be sidelined by ISO 9000. It is one of the fast-rising stars of the East, in its booming economy and privatization successes and in its adoption of world-class technology.

Up to 1990, Malaysian companies had to either bring in outsiders or acquire knowledge of ISO 9000 themselves, often by going on expensive overseas courses. The Malaysian government already had a national quality programme under way and an Industrial Technical Assistance Fund (ITAF) to help the development of small- and medium-size enterprises (SMEs), and this included both product development and quality. To this was added a scheme to grant aid to companies who employed local ISO 9000 consultants. By the end of 1988, five companies in Malaysia had achieved certification to ISO 9000. This rose to 142 at the end of 1992 and to 300 by the end of 1993. The applications for certification by 1995 suggest that exponential growth resulted in a doubling of the numbers certified to 600 at the end of 1994.

We can only speculate about the eventual growth of ISO 14000, but with sophisticated companies already implementing BS 7750 in anticipation of it, and with our existing awareness that environmental probity in manufacturing and services means quality products and services and their environmentally friendly production and delivery, it is a safe guess that ISO 14000 will have a spread equal to and perhaps greater than ISO 9000. Indeed, it may eventually encompass quality. This has already happened in the chemical industry, where quality is a minimum requirement and environment and safety the big issues.

Who needs the standards?

Most companies manufacturing products for sale in the developed world face the possibility that now or in the near future they must through independent certification demonstrate that their quality management systems conform to ISO 9000. The companies which will be first expected to conform are in the following categories of manufacturing:

- Suppliers of components or materials to manufacturing industry in general, in particular electronics, electrical, medical, pharmaceutical.
- Food and drink products.
- Building materials and components.
- Print and packaging.
- Transport, in particular specialized transport.
- Suppliers to the public procurement market.

While suppliers of services are not facing the same demands as those companies supplying materials and components, the requirement for service suppliers to hold ISO 9000 certification is growing, particularly from buyers in large multinational companies.

The initial drivers behind the quality and environmental management systems, represented by the standards ISO 9000 and ISO 14000, are different. The driver for ISO 9000 in Europe and elsewhere is customer or market, and, as such, is 'voluntary'; the driver for ISO 14000 is compliance with legislation. The voluntary nature of the first, however, extends only to those companies which are so large that they are selling to world consumer markets, but, even so, such companies are amongst the first to adopt it. Where a large buyer is demanding it, its voluntary nature is academic, and means only that it is not required by law. Although market is the initial driver for ISO 9000, it also has some aspects which are compliance driven, chiefly in the product liability and consumer information areas. US companies may not altogether share the market–driven motivation for ISO 9000, as within the US market legal conformance appears to be the main driver for both standards.

The main driver for environmental management systems, represented by such standards as BS 7750 and ISO 14000, is compliance with regulations. With their facility for managing compulsory environmental, health and safety, and public and product safety legislation, the environmental management standards provide comfortable assurance of legal compliance.

Relationships with other standards

The quality and environmental management standards, ISO 9000 and ISO 14000, both invented by BSI in its BS 5750 and BS 7750 versions, are the world's first management system standards – that is, as distinct from product and process standards. It can be taken for granted that in any company where ISO 9000 and ISO 14000 are implemented, the specific products and processes involved already conform to their own standards. For example, within a concrete product manufacturing company, it is hardly worthwhile to have a quality management system if the concrete is not manufactured to the standard for concrete.

Certification regimes in Europe now demand that an ISO 9000 quality management system be in place before certain products can be certified as meeting their standard – for example, those with critical safety elements, such as products in the EU requiring the CE Mark, a special mark denoting that all the tests required by law have been passed.

An apparent shortcoming in both standards, at least in ISO 9000 and the early drafts of ISO 14000, is that, while allowing for staff health and safety, they do not demand that these be managed under the standards, and they are lukewarm in their emphases on process, public and product safety. The reason for not incorporating staff health and safety may be that departments of labour tend to have separate health and safety powers including those of inspection, while the national standards bodies relate to departments of industry. This lack of emphases on vital safety matters, which pose legal threats for companies, is not reflected by the many companies who want to manage these issues under the standards, and least of all by the chemical industry, whose sensible plea is that the standards properly accommodate these issues.

3

ISO 9000

What is it?

ISO/TC 176 is the ISO committee which produced ISO 9000 and is responsible for its development. Here is the ISO/TC explanation of what ISO 9000 is.

> The ISO 9000 series is first and foremost an integrated, global system for optimizing the quality effectiveness of a company or organization, by creating a framework for continuous improvement.

This statement was created by ISO from a précis of different statements made at a Budapest 1993 plenary meeting of ISO/TC 176, so even the members of the committee, the architects of the series, needed help in defining ISO 9000.

The Budapest meeting produced the following caveat also.

> A company should achieve third–party registration/certification to ISO 9001, ISO 9002 or ISO 9003, for marketing, contractual or regulatory purposes, only when there has been 100 per cent implementation of ISO 9004, the quality management model.

At the meeting the chairman of ISO TC 176, Reg Shaughnessy, told delegates that there was

> a wide variation of understanding in the marketplace about what the standards were all about, and widely differing interpretations from the consulting industry.

A possible reason for this is that much of what is said by people on the ISO committees, such as TC 176, is not really fully comprehensible to people in industry who are willing to listen. One has to search constantly for clues, picking up the occasional remark which may make sense. Shaughnessy himself appeared to admit this at the session when he added:

> I find sometimes that because we have so many experts together for a week at our meetings, and because we have a good debate, we go away satisfied with having created good understanding; yet we haven't taken our message to the marketplace.

At this point he announced the intention to produce a simple brochure explaining the use of the ISO 9000 series. It had taken six years to come up with the idea of an explanatory brochure for the ISO 9000 series, 13 years since the commencement of work on the standards.

The brochure did appear subsequently, and it tells us that we should use ISO 9000–1 and ISO 9004–1 to guide us in our implementation of a quality management system, and ISO 8402 for an understanding of the terminology, and then, and only then, should we employ ISO 9001, ISO 9002 or ISO 9003 for *external* quality assurance purposes. Apparently companies are embracing ISO 9001 and ISO 9002 in response to market demands for certification and ignoring ISO 9000 and ISO 9004.

Worse still, in the eyes of the standard's architects, they are using checklists, mainly obtained from consultants and based on ISO 9001 and ISO 9002, to obtain certification rather than to achieve real systems of quality improvement. But companies should not be blamed for this as one must use 9001 and 9002 for certification purposes; if no-one is demanding certification, one can employ the principles of 9000 and 9004. The reader who has patiently taken all this in now needs to be told that the actual numbers of the last two standards have been expanded with sub numbers as shown below since the 1994 Phase One revisions, but are still referred to familiarly as ISO 9000 and ISO 9004 Part 1. (Part 2 is for services.)

Here is a simplified list of the ISO 9000 family of standards:

ISO 8402. This is the vocabulary of terms used in the series.
ISO 9000–1 is an update of ISO 9000.
ISO 9000–2 gives guidelines for the use of ISO 9001, 9002 and 9003.
ISO 9000–3 is for the software industry.
ISO 9000–4 is for dependability management.
ISO 9004–1 is an update of ISO 9004.
ISO 9004–2 is for the services sector.

ISO 9004–3 is for processed material.
ISO 9004–4 is for quality improvement.
ISO 9004–5 is a guideline for quality plans.
ISO 9004–6 is for project management.
ISO 9004–7 is for configuration management.
ISO 10011–1
–2
–3 are the guidelines for auditing.
ISO 10012–1 is for measuring equipment requirements.
ISO 10013–still in draft form, is for writing quality manuals.

ISO 9001, 9002 and 9003

The three standards, ISO 9001, ISO 9002 and ISO 9003, are simple enough to understand, and they are chosen for specific applications, and in particular for demonstration of compliance to customers, after the employment of ISO 9000 and ISO 9004.

ISO 9001

This is for companies who need to assure their customers that conformity to specified requirements is met throughout the whole cycle from design to service. It is the most complete and demanding of the series and applies in particular in contract situations. In it all the requirements of ISO 9004–1 are expected to be met stringently.

ISO 9002

Where design or specification is established, either internally or from the customer, this model is used to demonstrate capabilities in production and installation. It is less stringent than ISO 9001.

ISO 9003

This model is for the demonstration of capabilities in inspection and test where the product is supplied by a manufacturer for those purposes. It has an even lower level of stringency than ISO 9002 and may be eliminated in the Phase Two revisions.

A simple way to put it is that if you are looking for external certification because it is demanded by a customer, you will use ISO 9001, ISO 9002 or ISO 9003. If you simply want to embrace the ISO 9000 way you can do it with ISO 9000 and ISO 9004.

Doing your own thing is wrong

In 1993, the ISO/TC 176 committee passed a resolution asking users to stop referencing individual clauses or sections in the ISO 9000 standard, but, instead, to reference the individual standard in its entirety. The reason was the committee's concern about

> the proliferation of quality management system standards being proposed that transform the generic guidelines of the series into specific ones for individual technologies.

Enquiries about what the committee really meant were not fully satisfactory, so the author assumed that what was being talked about was either specific industry standards, such as software, or the tendency of some industries, and certifiers, to get away from the generic essence of ISO 9000 and to customize the standard down to application steps. The fact that one has to make such assumptions is a further indication of how confusing messages are from TC 176.

The following comment came from the chairman, Reg Shaughnessy:

> If individual groups prepared their own version of an ISO 9000 standard, the benefits of standardization, with the associated certification/registration programmes, would be lost and this would incur a very significant increase in costs.

He went on to warn against possible differences in regional interpretation and practices, or the development of 'product-specific' systems.

All of this seems to be saying, use the standard in the generic way it is intended, and do not make industry specific rules; and, to be of use, this criticism should be applied to the *certifiers* who are demanding industry specific rules – but who has the clout to do this? However, as it was still not clear if this is what TC 176 is really saying, the author wrote to TC 176.

The committee secretary, Peter Ford, replied on behalf of himself and Reg Shaughnessy, in a friendly letter, which included Reg Shaughnessy's home address and telephone number in Canada. The reply was in the form of the most recent paper given by Shaughnessy at an ISO conference in Washington. The key paragraph in the address is as follows.

> By working co-operatively, by using well established ISO liaison functions, it is expected that the product or service standards in these fields will normatively reference the appropriate ISO 9000 standards. It is also expected that product/technology/service standards will normatively reference guidance documents which will have been produced co-operatively under formal liaison arrangements between ISO/TC 176 and the relevant product technical committee and may, where appropriate, also normatively reference supplementary requirements for regulatory purposes which are not contained in the ISO 9000 system. By following this route and working co-operatively with other bodies, ISO Central Secretariat, CASCO [Council Committee on Conformity Assessment] together with those developing global supervision for third-party systems, we believe that the intended usefulness and applicability of the ISO 9000 series will be maintained and improved as we approach and go beyond the year 2000. There are a number of clarifications that are necessary but the cost to individual enterprises of developing and maintaining a third-party international system must be minimized and affordable to all sectors of business and industry, particularly for the small business community. We also have to provide an ever improving base upon which individual enterprises can build internal TQM [total quality management] systems that result in excellence in product and management performance. On the other hand, it cannot be relegated to a system of principles and concepts.

And finally in the letter from Peter Ford was the following paragraph:

> You raise the question of the undesirability of product standards referencing 'specific clauses'. Our standards represent a consensus on quality systems and we need to emphasize a reference to the complete system as crafted, and avoid the optional, indiscriminate choice of single elements because this would degrade the system from an implementable, standardized, code of management practice to simple menu status. This is illustrated in Reg's remarks re 'normatively' referencing the appropriate standard; our [TC 176] obligation is to provide an international standard, not an arbitrary specification from which arbitrary choices are made.

This could mean that we can use the ISO 9000 standards as a generic guide to applying a management system to our own industry code of practice. It could also mean that if you do not have a specific industry practice included in your system, that the certifier cannot introduce it under his or her interpretation of ISO 9000 (that is, where the certifier has seen what he/she believes to be better practices in similar companies elsewhere and is demanding their implementation).

Our difficulty is compounded by the fact that ISO can reply to us that ISO does not certify. But ISO is now talking about the need for its involvement in the establishment of unified certification procedures.

As if to put the reality in perspective, we have seen that if TC 176 does not want specific codes of practice for ISO 9000, BSI has already produced them for

BS 5750/ISO 9000 and has begun the same process for BS 7750, and they are extremely useful.

The BSI codes of practice for BS 5750/ISO 9000

BSI probably leads the field in supplying codes of practice for specific industries, and it is difficult to see how such codes are not a huge benefit to companies attempting to implement both ISO 9000 and ISO 14000, as they specify the actual quality or environmental issues to be addressed within each of the industries they apply to.

To implement a meaningful quality or environmental management system, one needs to adhere to the generic requirements of the relevant standard and, at the same time, address the specific elements of one's process. For example, if you are a transport company, you need to know the quality and environmental issues which are relevant to you, and if you are a print and packaging company you need to know the environmental implications of the materials you are using. These are the questions the codes answer.

The codes are cross-referenced to the relevant process or system paragraphs of ISO 9001 and ISO 14001, which are all under Section 4. It is Section 4, and all the clauses and sub-clauses under it in each of the main standards (ISO 9001, ISO 9002, and ISO 14001) which specify the requirements for the quality or environmental management system. Other sections deal with issues such as policy, organization, auditing, and so on. Section 4 is, therefore, one which specifies both the system and the structure of the Quality Manual and Environmental Manual. When the certifying inspector arrives on site, he or she takes a checklist approach to ensuring that all of the requirements of Section 4 are satisfied.

ISO 9001 also serves as ISO 9002 with the non-relevant sections such as design ignored. What you do is create a generic quality or environmental management standard such as those suggested in this book and add the relevant bits of the code of practice to the numbered paragraphs. If you are fortunate enough to find one for your industry, fine-tune it to your own specific company requirements. Make sure to also put in place the procedures which the expanded paragraphs in Figure 3.1 now describe, these being the list of BSI, and some other, codes of practice for BS 5750/ISO 9000.

(The codes of practice applicable to BS 7750 are discussed later in this book, see Chapter 6.)

Figure 3.1 Codes of practice for BSI and some other institutions

Industry/sector	*Title*
Hotel and catering industry	BSI code of practice for BS 5750
Transport and storage and distribution	BSI code of practice for BS 5750
Banking and finance	BSI code of practice for BS 5750
Education and training	BSI code of practice for BS 5750
Solicitors	The Law Society (UK) code of practice based on BS 5750
Accountants	No BSI code of practice but standard accounting code which should be available from accounting institutes
Car dealers	BSI code of practice for BS 5750
Security installers	BSI code of practice for BS 5750

The ISO 9000 Forum

A very user-friendly organization, the ISO 9000 Forum, is operated by ISO and based in Geneva. Its main vehicle is its newsletter, the *ISO 9000 News*. There are six issues per year featuring up-to-date information about some of the following:

- The ISO 9000 series standards, their development and probable future revisions.
- Adopting and applying the ISO 9000 series in company quality assurance initiatives.
- Setting up and operating independent third-party certification or registration procedures to acknowledge conformity with ISO 9000 standards.
- Information sources on training programmes for quality managers, and quality systems auditors.
- Developing means to achieve multinational recognition of ISO 9000 standards conformance based on recognition in one country.
- Upcoming and newsworthy events, a quality management calendar relating to management systems: symposia, awards, workshops, conferences.
- Access to international seminars, books and other media.

While *ISO 9000 News* is the most valuable device, the Forum also supplies other useful information from time to time, including press releases, special notices about updates to the standard and explanatory brochures. Members also receive the monthly general *ISO Bulletin* which carries interesting news about both ISO 9000 and the developing ISO 14000 (which the Forum also reports on), and all the other main developments in standardization. In addition, *ISO 9000 News* also supplies fascinating information about the developments in ISO 9000 and certification schemes in countries all around the world. The annual subscription is CHP 450 (Swiss francs). The address is:
The ISO 9000 Forum
ISO Central Secretariat
1, rue Varembe, 1211 Geneva 20
The Forum's fax number is + 41 22 734 10 79.

ISO 9000 support groups

There are ISO 9000 support groups in the US, Europe and around the world. These groups provide an independent arena for discussion, advice, and information exchange. Their primary mission is to assist companies, to promote a better understanding of the standard and the steps involved in implementation, the benefits of registration, and the process of becoming registered.

The groups in the US and Europe also support ISO 14000 and BS 7750 and the EMAS regulation. The US group has a bulletin board which can be accessed over the Internet, which the European group is linked to also. The European group is a spin-off from, and partner with, the US group. Both publish newsletters and regular updates. The US group address is:
The US National ISO 9000 Support Group
9964 Cherry Valley
Building #2
Caledonia, MI 49316
USA.

ISO 9000 certification

There is no such thing as 'ISO certification', despite the fact that it is talked about all over the world. Any one of us, individual or corporate body, can implement an

ISO 9000 quality management system and declare that we are operating to ISO 9000. To achieve this we will use ISO 9004 and ISO 9000, and subsets where necessary; when, however, a customer, whom we wish to continue to supply, asks us for third-party corroboration that we have achieved the requirements of the standard, we have to employ ISO 9001 or ISO 9002, and subject ourselves to inspection from a certifying agency in the hope that we achieve certification. (See Chapter 20 for fuller information on certification.)

4

The ISO 9000 documentation

Introduction

There are three levels of documentation needed in ISO 9000, and these are often referred to as levels 1, 2 and 3.

The top level is the Quality Manual, which is shown in detail in Appendix 1.

The second level is made up of all the specific documents needed to control the issues which are fundamental to quality. Examples include: quality plans, measurement and testing routines, inspection and test records, customer specifications, customer performance, supplier/vendor specifications, sales order processing procedure.

The third, and lowest, level is made up of the standard operating procedures, known as the SOPs. The titles of the SOPs are placed in an index ahead of, or at the beginning of, the Quality Manual.

The documents involved

A useful check on the comprehensiveness of the quality management system in meeting the requirements of ISO 9000 is to ensure that:

1. The Quality Manual is as complete as the sample in Appendix 1.
2. It reflects the real situation and is not just a paper exercise.
3. All of the other necessary support documentation is in place, using the broad list which follows in the document index (see below). This list is basic, and one's own company situation will need these documents expanded or added to, but a cursory glance may reveal what is missing. If there are documents mentioned here which cannot be found in your company there should be a good reason.

The other documentation

Apart from these quality management system documents, you need the following:

1. Task procedures related to shop floor and connected activities – that is, exact instructions for your product and activities.
2. Health and safety procedures. (See the list of SOPs with the Health and Safety Manual in Chapter 13.)

Organizing the factory

We now have the names of all the documents and the Quality Manual. Samples of what else we need follow, but these must be made specific to each inspection. We need to set out or reorganize the factory to reflect the demands of the standard as expressed in the Quality Manual. In particular, the following will apply:

- Segregation of goods inward. A separate fenced-off or marked-off goods inward inspection area. Segregated areas and labelling/marking systems for pass/fail/hold. These areas and systems can be green, amber and red marked as necessary.
- Stores off limits except to personnel named at the stores access point.
- Inventory control.
- Production control.
- Quality check points identified and an initialling or signing system for operators passing component between such points.
- Inspection and test routines.
- A finished goods area.
- A calibration and testing system for monitoring equipment.

All the documents should be listed in a document index (see next section) which can be one of the first pages of the Quality Manual.

Document index

The documents listed here (see Figure 4.1 on this and following page) are a mixture of control records and procedures/instructions. They are intended to illustrate how such documents must back up the Quality Manual and be referenced to it. Where reference is made to a procedure, such as non-conforming procedures, these procedures also contain records, such as non-conforming material, or non-conforming component.

Of course, were we to try to include all possible documents, this book would be full of documents not relevant to every company and equally full of partially blank

Figure 4.1 Document numbers by title (*continued on next page*)

Document number	*Title*
DC–01	Document master list
DC–02	Amendment list
DC–03	Circulation list
DC–04	Organization chart
QM–01	Quality manual
QP–01	Quality plans (overview of inspection, test, audit and review procedures)
MT–01	Measurement and testing routines
IT–01	Inspection and test records
CS–01	Customer specifications
CP–01	Customer performance
SP–01	Supplier/vendor specifications
SP–02	Supplier/purchasing procedures
SP–03	Approved vendor list
SO–01	Sales order processing procedure
CCR–01	Records of contract reviews
DP–01	Design procedures
PDP–01	Product design and development plan
PC–01	Product catalogues
PS–01	Product specification

continued overleaf

Figure 4.1 continued

Document number	*Title*
QF–01	Quote file
SP–01	Safety procedures
SOP–01	Operating procedures
SOP–02	
–03	
–09	
SOP–00	Special process procedures
IN–01	Inspection procedures, including goods inwards, goods inward inspection (GII) and in–process inspection and testing procedure. (These can be in the operating procedures.)
ST–01	Stores procedures
QP–01	Non-conforming procedures
QP–02	Corrective action procedure
QP–03	Non-conforming product review and disposition procedure
CT–01	Calibration and testing of equipment
QP–22	Quality records
QP–23	Training procedure
QP–01	Internal audits
QP–36	Management review
HD–01	Handling and delivery
SC–01	Statistical control procedures
SR–01	Servicing procedures (if any)

pages. Companies will therefore use their own numbering system. (This latter system is explained more fully later in this chapter: see below, 'Important note'.)

Sundry other documents

These will include company minutes and departmental reports, notes of managers' meetings and associated documents (Figure 4.2).

Figure 4.2 Sundry other documents

SD–01	Management review meetings
SD–02	Details of any product which is recalled
SD–03	Customer returns
SD–04	Customer complaints
SD–05	Details of disposal/scrap and non-conforming product(s)
SD–06	Details of any internal/external quality audits
SD–07	Records of statistical analysis or pass/fail quantities and fault descriptions
SD–08	Calibration records
SD–09	Certificates of conformance
SD–10	Product approvals
SD–11	The supporting control records
SD–12	Audit checklist
SD–13	Employee training log
SD–14	Product recall
SD–15	Tendering procedures

Important note

The above are sample procedures only, given as representative examples of what procedures are needed. Your own procedures will be determined by the products and processes employed, as well as by your house style and existing documentation regime.

For the control function, however, three basic elements are needed: What is the job and its controls? Who is doing it? What is the status and when was it done?

These elements should be reflected in control documents which have such headings as:

Job	Check employed	Operator initials	Date

Other important control documents will simply reflect the overall status of checks and inspections, acting as logs.

Phase One revisions

In 1994 the Phase One Revisions to ISO 9000 were published. In most countries certification agencies expected these to have been made to existing systems during

1995 at the latest. Readers new to the standard can adopt the Quality Manual in Appendix 1 and adapt it to their needs, as it reflects the Phase One revisions, but those with pre-Phase One versions need to compare their manuals either paragraph by paragraph with a 1994 version of ISO 9001 or ISO 9002 or with the manual in Appendix 1. The following is a summary of what the Phase One changes were:

ISO 9000: 1987	became ISO 9000–1 (first of several parts)
ISO 9004: 1987	became ISO 9004–1 (first of several parts)
ISO 9001, 9002 and 9003	remain ISO 9001, 9002, and 9003

There are five core standards, which are:

ISO 9000–1	Guidelines
9001	
9002	
9003	
9004–1	Guidelines

The full set at the time of writing is:

ISO 8402	Terminology
ISO 9000–1	Guidelines for selection and use
ISO 9000–2	Guidelines for the application of ISO 9001, 9002, and 9003
ISO 9000–3	Guidelines for the application of ISO 9001 to the development, supply and maintenance of software
ISO 9000–4	Guide to dependability programme management
ISO 9001	The three standards for use in external verification, such as certification
ISO 9002	
ISO 9003	
ISO 9004–1	Quality management and quality system elements – Guidelines
ISO 9004–2	Guidelines for services
ISO 9004–3	Guidelines for processed materials
ISO 9004–4	Guidelines for quality improvement
ISO 9004–5	Guidelines for quality plans
ISO 9004–6	(still at CD stage) Quality management and quality system elements – project management

ISO 9004–7	Guidelines for configuration management
ISO 10011–1	Auditing
ISO 10011–2	Qualification criteria for quality system auditors
ISO 10011–3	Management of audit programmes
ISO 10012–1	Metrological configuration system for measuring equipment

Note that the standards for auditing the ISO 9000 systems are in the ISO 10000 series.

Background to the Phase Two revisions

The Phase One Revisions of the ISO 9000 series were published in 1994, and they are reflected in the headings of the sample Quality Manual in Appendix 1.

In 1990 a task force commissioned by TC 176 to prepare a strategic plan for ISO 9000 came up with the report, *Vision 2000.* TC 176 adopted the principles of this report, paving the way for a two-phase restructuring of the ISO 9000 series, the first phase by 1994, the second within the next few years and within the decade. The task force also produced recommendations for the related ISO 10000 series on auditing.

The task force identified a number of critical issues to be dealt with. The first was the proliferation of standards. It warned that if the ISO 9000 series was to become a mere nucleus of a proliferation of local standards derived, but varying in contents and form, from the original, there would be little worldwide standardization. In a related sentence it added that the growth of localized certification schemes would create further complications.

The author believes that neither *Vision 2000* nor TC 176 have dealt adequately with this issue. We are left with the warning that localization or customization of the generic standard is wrong, despite the fact that it is virtually impossible to implement a practical management system without recourse to an industry standard. While the task force has admitted that the problem can be exacerbated by certification schemes, the author believes that certification schemes are the principal cause of the problem. Certification agencies may appoint inspectors because of a background in a specific industry; these inspectors may subsequently demand strict adherence to industry, or even specific company, codes of practice and use their own industry specific checklists for the requirements of every paragraph in the 'system' sections of ISO 9001 and ISO 14001.

In their recommendation the *Vision 2000* team say: 'There should be no industry/economic sector – specific external quality system standards used as the assessment documents for such certification schemes.'

The author has seen companies failed for ISO 9000 certification, and on inspecting the assessment report found clear evidence in the list of reasons for the failure that the inspector had employed his or her own checklist of industry specific requirements.

The Phase One Revisions accepted that there were industry/economic sectors and sought to define these as hardware, software, process materials and services, and, indeed, we now have sub–sections of ISO 9000 dealing with each of these. However, even as this solution was being adopted, TC 176 believed that such sections were merging (hardware and software for example) and that Phase Two would have to accommodate such a development.

The vision, therefore, for Phase Two was the development of a single quality management standard, in an updated ISO 9004, for internal purposes, and, for external assurance, or certification, an external quality assurance standard, an updated ISO 9001, with an ISO 9002 subset. Supplementary standards would merely offer expanded guidance.

The original target dates were 1992 for Phase One and 1996 for Phase Two. Phase One was finally published in 1994; Phase Two will not see publication by 1996, particularly as it has since been referred to as ISO 9000: 1999.

So much for the development of ISO 9000, but what about its relationship with ISO 14000? By 1994 meetings were taking place between TC 207, environment, and TC 176, quality. A three–phase plan was drawn up as follows:

1. Short term. Compatibility between the 1994 ISO 9000 and the 1995 ISO 14000 series of documents.
2. Medium term. Compatibility between the 1995 ISO 14000 and the 1999 (Phase Two) ISO 9000 series.
3. Long term. The harmonization of all standards within the ISO 9000 and ISO 14000 series.

The long-term objective may reflect the interest of a number of the standards architects to develop a general management standard, but notably missing even from Phase Two are the health and safety issues.

Accreditation bodies, such as the NACCB in the UK, are now also persuading certification bodies to avoid a checklist approach to certification and to ensure that companies identify and manage the significant issues whether these be direct (on site) or indirect in the supply chain above or below the site, and whether they be pollution or resource usage based.

This is very sensible and should help reduce the tendency towards checklist certification, but it does not resolve the conflict between TC 176's warnings against industry specific versions and industry's need to be specific; if anything it increases the tendency to be industry specific, as environmental issues are similar within industrial sectors.

Developing the quality manual

The quality manual has become the centrepiece of the ISO 9000 series. It contains the company's quality policy and a description of its quality system. It has evolved into a document which both slavishly addresses the systems section (Section 4) of ISO 9001, or an ISO 9002 or ISO 9003 subset, and also acts as the top-level reference document to all subsidiary procedures and control documents.

It is the basis for the checklists (criticized by members of ISO/TC committees) which are used both to develop the full system and to demonstrate compliance with the requirements of the standard to a certifying inspector.

In an ideal world, the quality manual would be written last, after a good system adhering to the recommendations of ISO 9000 and ISO 9004 Part 1 has been implemented. In practice, people begin with the quality manual and work downwards, producing both the documents and the shop floor procedures from it, and, as is remarked elsewhere in this book, however far below the ideal that may be it is a thoroughly practical approach.

Thus, the emergence of both generic quality manuals and generic quality manuals customized to specific industries. The author has produced practical customized quality manuals derived from generic models for the following sectors: general manufacturing, chemicals, food, print and packaging, transport and distribution, waste management and generic services.

ISO has now made a contribution to the development of the quality manual by originating a standard (still at the discussion stage at the time of writing) known as *Guidelines for developing quality manuals*. The number is ISO/DIS 10013 (the 'DIS' stands for discussion). Somewhat confusingly, the ISO 10000 series is also for auditing quality systems.

This standard makes an interesting distinction between various kinds of quality manual – such as quality manual, quality management manual and quality assurance manual – distinctions which do not appear to be very helpful. The assurance model would be used for external purposes, while the management one would be retained internally. It seems practical to adopt a single 'quality manual'.

What this somewhat overly legal and formal document, ISO/DIS 10013, tells us is that the quality manual records and presents the basic documentation used for planning and managing the quality system. It tries to maintain a fine line between urging completeness and not getting into technical detail, such as work instructions. It specifies the all–important section 'subclause 4.1', which is referred to elsewhere in this book as 'Section 4'. What companies actually do is re-write the Section 4 clauses of ISO 9001, or its 9002 and 9003 versions, into their own quality manuals tailoring them to their needs, and cross-referencing their own paragraphs (which may not be numbered 4) to the subclause 4.1 paragraphs of the standard, as shown in our sample quality manual in Appendix 1.

According to ISO/DIS 10013, the purposes of the quality manual are the implementation and management of the quality system and its presentation where necessary to external bodies for demonstration of compliance with the ISO 9000 series of standards. While the elements in Section 4 should be addressed, there is in fact no ISO requirement for either the structure or format of a quality manual; one would, however, be rash not to adhere to Section 4.

The issue and change control procedure for quality manuals must be tightly controlled. This is usually done by a document control table either on the contents or a separate page, which gives details of revision status. Where a copy of the manual is not controlled it should be stamped 'uncontrolled copy'.

In addition to Section 4 information, the quality manual should contain a title, a description of the scope and field of the quality system, contents list, company information, the policy, the organization, and appendices as required.

A broad structure for a quality manual which would appear to satisfy the requirements of ISO/DIS 10013 could be:

1. The title and heading section.
2. The policy.
3. Field of application/scope/purpose.
4. The organization and responsibilities.
5. The system (Section 4).
6. Documents, records, controls (or references to them).

5

ISO 9000 and the chemical industry

The chemical industry has an excellent code of practice which can be used by all process companies as the guiding or top-level policy. This is the Responsible Care Programme (RCP), discussed in Chapter 14 and in the Preface.

The European federation of chemical industry associations, CEFIC, and its UK member body the CIA (Chemical Industry Association), have been using both ISO 9000 and BS 7750 to manage the RCP in Europe. This seems particularly true of the CIA. The chemical industry in Europe, and in particular the UK, has also been championing the use of ISO 9000 to cover quality, environment and health and safety.

Despite the highly commendable efforts which the chemical industry has put into developing an expanded ISO 9000 (ISO 9001 to be precise) to cover quality, environmental protection, staff health and safety, and process and product safety, it now seems that this approach will not be adopted. There are several reasons for this, chief among them the emergence of ISO 14000 and the publishing of new rules for the accreditation of certification agencies in respect of the environmental standard, by bodies such as the NACCB in the UK.

It now appears that the BS 7750/ISO 14000 road is the only one for obtaining certification of a company's environmental management system. This may not be all bad news for the chemical industry, as the RCP has been criticized by environmental activists as being a system of self-certification.

In the EU it is very difficult to meet the requirements of the EMAS regulation without a certified environmental management system, based on BS 7750/ISO 14000, so the industry can now use the certified environmental standard to demonstrate compliance with both the RCP and EMAS, thus achieving the third part corroboration demanded by its critics.

The chemical industry has been trying to persuade the international community to use a single ISO generic management system standard which covers safety, health and the environment, and is compatible with quality. The industry sees this as satisfying a number of requirements including those of the RCP. It also sees the system as an environment, health and safety system, supporting the RCP which, as noted in the Preface, the industry calls SHEM (safety, health and environmental management). The pity is that while most companies would agree with the chemical industry that SHEM is relevant, the architects of the ISO and BSI standards have treated the staff health and safety issue as optional.

With ISO at last looking at health and safety, and the BSI already doing so in a possible BS 8750 guideline, we may soon see that generic management system standard sought by the chemical industry, beginning with a BS 9750, but this is still speculation.

The CIA guidelines for ISO 9001

The CIA has published the most comprehensive document on using ISO 9000 to meet environmental and safety requirements, *Guidelines for certification to ISO 9001: health, safety and environmental management systems (and BS 7750 – environmental management systems) in the chemical industry*.

An important point. The document was published by the CIA before the Phase One revisions to ISO 9000 were published, so the reader taking this approach should use the 1994 edition of ISO 9001 (as shown in Appendix 1) if updating the standard with the extra material shown below. (The reason this book has not done so is explained in the comments at the start and end of this chapter.)

The key to understanding the relationship between the ISO 9000 series, BS 5750, BS 7750, and the CIA guidelines is in the section of each standard numbered four (as in 4.1, 4.2), as this is the section which specifies the system requirements. In the case of ISO 9000, the paragraphs of Section 4 can be taken to represent also the requirements of the Quality Manual. Certifying inspectors tend to use the paragraphs of Section 4 for their detailed audits, a practice which has resulted in the criticized 'certification checklists' approach. The French AFNOR 30-200 environmental management standard also uses Section 4 for the systems requirement.

Here is a summary of how the CIA uses ISO 9001 to satisfy the RCP requirements on health, safety and environment (H,S&E). Interested readers should obtain the full CIA guideline document mentioned above. The title of Section 4 in this document is *Occupational health, safety and environment (H,S&E) system requirement.* The following summary should be read as constituting what additions are being made to ISO 9001 to achieve the H,S&E requirement.

H,S&E policy (health, safety and environment)

H,S&E are stated as priority functions. The RCP documents are to be used. The meeting of statutory requirements including hazard identification and risk control are expressed as policy. A public statement or publication on H,S&E is required.

Organization
This is normal except that it now includes H,S&E.

Management review
This is normal and includes H,S&E.

Management systems
This sees the H,S&E manual as the top document, whereas it is the Quality Manual in ISO 9001, and the Environmental Management Manual in BS 7750/ISO 14000. The H,S&E and SOPs could be used in the CIA system but elevated to the place of the Environmental Management Manual.

Contract review
This is seen as the obligation for the organization to establish and meet the objectives of policy and statutory requirements. The areas listed read very like the US version of RCP management codes published by the CMA (the US chemical manufacturer's association). They include:

- Emissions.
- Resource conservation.
- Product stewardship.
- Safety – staff and public.

The codes appear not to include distribution which is included in the US version of RCP.

Design control
This includes establishing H,S&E criteria, hazard identification and risk assessment, legislative requirements and monitoring.

Document control
This is similar to ISO 9000/ISO 14000.

Purchasing
This simply includes H,S&E issues in the procurement procedures.

Purchaser supplied product
This is similar to ISO 9000/ISO 14000.

Product identification and traceability
This is similar to ISO 9000/ISO 14000.

Process control
This is a H,S&E version of process control and introduces the concept of hazard data sheets and the COSHH regulations (the chemical industry's occupational safety rules for the handling of hazardous substances).

Inspection and testing
This is the heart of the CIA approach, for what it does is to use the ISO 9000 inspection and test requirements, formerly seen only as 'quality' tests to inspect and test all the environmental and health and safety issues. Chemical manufacturers who separate the environmental/safety and quality issues could have problems with this, especially where there are separate managers and separate systems.

The CIA has demonstrated that such elements as process conditions, inspection of pressure vessels, atmosphere testing, noise levels, and analyses of flue gases and liquid discharges under inspection and test can be included. The monitoring of local flora and fauna and medical examinations are also included under final inspection and test, together with product analyses and verification of decontamination.

Inspection, measuring and test equipment
This is the same as ISO 9000/ISO 14000 with a strong H,S&E flavour.

Inspection and test results
This is the same as ISO 9000/ISO 14000.

Control of non-conforming products
This has been re-slanted to reflect control of processes, incidents, emergencies.

Corrective action
This is the same as ISO 9000/ISO 14000.

H,S&E records
This is the same as ISO 9000/ISO 14000.

Internal audits
This is the same as ISO 9000/ISO 14000.

Training
This is the same as ISO 9000/ISO 14000.

Servicing
This refers to the RCP Product Stewardship management code (the list of RCP codes is shown in Chapter 14), but does not appear to fully satisfy requirements which range from the definition of responsibilities to the publishing of policy and performance.

It sees 'service' as responsibility to community rather than servicing a customer.

Statistical techniques
This is the same in principle as ISO 9000/ISO 14000, but with a H,S&E bias.

Comments on the CIA approach

The main difficulty of using the CIA's ISO 9000 to satisfy environmental and health and safety requirements is that the expanded standard does not tell us everything we need to know about how to do it, despite having gone a long way towards it. What must however sound its death knell is that, in its new rules for the accreditation of certification agencies in respect of the environmental standard, the NACCB has clearly stated that for their first certification new environmental management systems in the UK must be separate from ISO 9000 and not add-ons to it, and this appears to scupper the CIA approach.

Chemical companies in the UK and elsewhere in Europe have been implementing their environmental management systems using both ISO 9000 and BS 7750. If they are to achieve the great benefits of 'certified' RCPs and of obtaining the EMAS logo and listing, it now appears that the BS 7750/ISO 14000 route is the only way to do so. Having examined the standards in detail, the author is convinced that the BS 7750/ISO 14000 route is the most practical and best way, despite the great efforts of the CIA and CEFIC to expand ISO 9001.

With the chemical industry facing hostile critics, and fighting for its image and its very existence in some countries, it must not pass up the opportunity of securing independent certification of its RCP through certified management standards.

6

ISO 14000 – the environmental management standard

On 6 April 1992, the BSI unveiled its second revolutionary management standard, BS 7750, *Environmental Management Systems*, the world's first environmental management standard. An important element in this development was the interest of the UK government's Department of Trade (DOT) as distinct from its Department of the Environment (DOE).

A strong department of trade, understanding the relevance of environmental management for industry and its exports can exercise some element of control over environmental matters, and in particular certification of the environmental performance of manufacturing plants, and not have these critical matters languish in departments of the environment, some of which in Europe have been notorious in their neglect of industrial environmental needs. Successive Irish ministers of the environment, for example, have sat on the fence and avoided taking any decisions on the disposal of industrial and medical toxic wastes for almost 20 years, despite Ireland's dependence for employment on these industries.

In the UK, the BSI has had a long association with environmental standards, going back over 30 years, and this was reflected in the development of BS 7750.

Just before its launch, Michael Heseltine MP, then Secretary of State for the Environment, said:

> A further important development is the work of the British Standards Institution in preparing an environmental management standard. This initiative will provide a detailed generic model of environmental management that any organization can use to develop its own internal management systems. It should thus fully complement the framework that the EC regulation is expected to provide and indeed should provide a means by which companies wishing to participate in the Community's Eco-Audit [EMAS] scheme could comply with some of its requirements. The approach is based on the successful work of the BSI in developing the BS 5750 standard for quality management. That standard was subsequently adopted as the basis for an international standard, ISO 9000. Clearly, there would be much to be gained for British business if the BSI environmental standard could again serve as an international starting point.

At that time, Bernardo Delogu of the EC Commission's DG X1 Environment, who had the responsibility for the development of the EMAS regulation, stated:

> If a UK standard is soon established, it is clear that it could later be easily transferred into a European standard . . . it could even be more important than ever before, being the obvious reference for future developments at EC level.

Shortly after both of these statements the BSI also declared that the standard would be compatible with European and international activities, and this appears to have been borne out both by the subsequent developments in the EMAS regulation and by those in ISO 14000. In addition, the BSI declared it to be modelled upon and related to ISO 9000.

From 1992, companies, first in the UK and Ireland and then elsewhere, began to implement BS 7750 as a standard which, in its own right, would give credence to the environmental probity of their activities, and also would allow third-party certification when the first such schemes became available. France followed with its own version AFNOR 30-200 (Systeme de management environnemental), and then Ireland with IS 310.

Until early 1995, no accredited certifiers were available as accreditation schemes were not yet in place. (This complex subject of certification and accreditation is dealt with in Chapter 17 and in another Gower book, *Standards and Certification in Europe*.) The BSI and other certifiers waited for an accredited scheme, but SGS Yarsley UK, a subsidiary of the large Swiss headquartered company SGS, began to certify companies by issuing its own Green Dove certificates, attesting to its belief that qualifying companies were indeed operating to the requirements of BS 7750. The reasons for this initiative were a combination of good marketing and the fact that SGS had one of the first lead assessors capable of environmental management auditing. The author was fortunate to have a dialogue with this person during the assessment of some of the first companies to be certified, which was a help in writing both the BS 7750 book and this one. The assessor was also an important conduit for information coming from the NACCB, which became the accreditor of the certifying bodies for the environmental standard early in 1995. (While the NACCB is involved mainly with accrediting UK certification companies, it can accredit others anywhere in the world.)

The elements involved in the environmental management standard

The early work with companies quickly revealed that the elements involved in the standard were more than the traditional environmental issues. Here is a general list of the traditional issues:

- Emissions to the air.
- Discharges to water resources.
- Water supplies and sewage treatment.
- Waste.
- Nuisances.
- Noise.
- Odours.
- Radiation.
- Amenity, trees and wildlife.
- Urban renewal.
- Physical planning.
- Environmental impact assessment.
- Packaging.
- Materials use.
- Energy use.

Over and above these traditional environmental issues environmental management could, and should, also relate to the important issues of:

- Product use.
- Product disposal.
- Process/public safety.
- Staff health and safety.

A good way to distinguish between quality and environment is to picture a plant manufacturing a quality ISO 9000-certified product, and doing it in an environmentally unfriendly and even dangerous way. This was possible for manufacturers, but not likely for services providers, as it is difficult, and often impossible, to provide a dirty and dangerous quality service. Thus, it is much easier for services companies to implement one system which covers both elements.

As the first companies began to implement BS 7750, it became apparent that where ISO 9000 was largely market driven, this standard was in the first instance compliance driven, as most of the issues required to be covered under it, and all the other issues which could be covered also, were driven by legislation with critical implications for management, some with a potential for personal liability.

Many were thus surprised at the lukewarm attention which both BS 7750 and early versions of ISO 14000 gave to the issue of staff health and safety, the inclusion of which was optional, and to the somewhat low priority given to process and public safety, and to product safety and disposal. As remarked already in earlier chapters, only the chemical industry seemed to fully appreciate the need to include these issues.

ISO 14000

The environmental management standard, ISO 14000, is still under development at the time of writing and expected to be completed, to final draft stage at least, during 1996. Like ISO 9000, it is in fact a series of standards. The series is explained in the sections which follow, but some basic points about how the reader should use this section now follow.

Readings of the early draft documents indicate that anyone who has taken BS 7750 in its most comprehensive sense and in particular anyone who has implemented an environmental management system to the requirements of the RCP, or at least in a manner which ensures that it covers such major elements as traditional environmental issues, process, public and product safety, and staff health and safety, should feel assured that the full requirements of ISO 14000 when it appears in its final form have been met.

The approach taken here is that discussed in Chapter 1, which is to ensure that all of the significant issues are so well managed that the system will be as good as, or better than, that required by the standard. Having said this, no-one can fully anticipate what has not yet been written, nor can they know what idiosyncrasies or bureaucratic rules may still be devised by the architects of the standard. The early drafts indicate that in general common sense prevails and one should expect this to continue. Examples of exceptions, discussed later, are in the ISO 14000 auditing standards.

How to use this section

This section tries to achieve a balance of a minimum amount of background and explanatory text and, within the indications imposed by a book, a maximum of advice on the documentation needed. Readers are once again reminded that, should they need them, full packages of generic documentation written to both the ISO 9000 and BS 7750 standards, are available from Gower.

Here is a practical guide to implementing the ISO 14000 standard.

1. Obtain a commitment from top management, presenting a proposal if necessary. Samples of such a proposal are available in textbooks on ISO 9000 and BS 7750, and in the documentation packages.
2. Carry out the Initial Environmental Review (IER) and build the Register of Regulations, along lines which follow later (see Chapters 7 and 8).
3. Once the IER and the Register of Regulations are complete, one is in the position of knowing both the law (including policies and codes of practice which may go beyond the law or apply to activities not covered by legislation) and the environmental status and probity of one's purchased materials, processes and products. Both of these are essentially passive documents, although the IER will indicate what needs to be done.
4. The first active step, and the most important, is the construction of the Environmental Management Programme (EMP). Neither BS 7750 nor the early drafts of ISO 14000 are clear about how this should be done, but an approach is proposed here which appears to work well in some of the first companies in the world to apply the standard.

   The approach is that the EMP is the total programme, including the implementation project with its IER, the construction of the Register of Regulations and the creation of the environmental management system (EMS).

   What is the difference between the EMP and EMS? The former includes the actual organization, environmental manager and environmental review team, the structure and agenda for the monthly meetings, the control of new programmes and the initial project, including the fixing of any once-off non-conformances discovered during the IER, the long-term targets and objectives, the publishing of policy and performance. The EMS is the day-to-day system, which may or may not be largely automated. The EMP is documented (as shown shortly), and it reviews documents and controls in the EMS. The EMS is largely the Register of Environmental Effects, a sub-document known as the Effects Evaluation Procedure (subordinate to the EMP), the Control and Monitoring Manual and the Environmental Management Manual, and all related operating procedures and controls.

5. The environmental management system. Once the IER, the Register of Regulations, and the Environmental Management Programme (EMP) are in place, the Effects Evaluation Procedure can take place. This is largely once-off by nature and carried out during the initial project, but it must be repeated for each new product, process or programme which could have significant environmental effects.

   The Register of Environmental Effects is perhaps the most important document. Where the Register of Regulations is a passive statement of what the law and policies demand, this is the document which details the actual impact of the company's activities on the environment. It is a list of issues and their effects and potential effects. It reflects both direct (in-house or under the direct control of the company) and indirect (such as purchased materials) issues and their pollution and resource usage effects.

   The Control and Monitoring Manual, the basis of which can be both in hard copy and automated, is the set of documents, all signed, which demonstrate that management is controlling the significant issues, while the Environmental Management Manual is the top-level document, the quality manual of the environmental management system.

   For legal reasons, while one can, and usually does, control staff health and safety under the EMS, it should be documented separately in a Health and Safety Manual, and supported by SOPS (as shown in Chapter 13).

   A staff training course is required as is a system of audits and reviews.

ISO 14000 has introduced a system of product life cycle assessment, which, while suggested, had not been formalized in BS 7750.

All of these are now covered in the relevant sections which follow, but first the position with the different sections of ISO 14000 is given.

The ISO 14000 series in detail

The technical committee carrying out the development of the ISO 14000 series is TC 207 and the secretariat is held by the Standards Council of Canada (SCA). A number of sub-committees in various parts of the world operate under this main committee, each responsible for discrete functions within the standard, each of which will have a sub-standard with its own number within the ISO 14000 series.

ISO 14000: 1995 series

At the time of going to press, this was the situation with the emerging series.

ISO 14000 Environmental management systems (SC1)

1. Specification: core verifiable elements, such as 9002. Published by ISO as the *2nd Preliminary draft of Environmental Management System specification.*
2. General principles and guidance: a broader view, such as 9000–4. Published as *Guide to Environmental Management Principles, Systems and Supporting Technique (V 62 13/7/94) ISO 14 xxx.*

ISO 14001 Environmental management systems

This key document, *Specification with guidance for use*, is the equivalent to ISO 9001.

ISO 1410 Environmental auditing (SC2)

Three documents are planned for publication in1995:

1. General principles	ISO/CD 1410.
2. Procedures	14011 - 1.
3. Qualification criteria for auditors	14012.
and a fourth	
4. Environmental site assessments	is expected after 1995.

Environmental labelling (EC) SC3

Two documents are underway.

1. Principles and practices.
2. Terms and definitions.

Environmental performance evaluation (EPE) SC4

A framework document now exists. The first private committee document version of a generic EPE standard is expected in June 1996. The technical committee needs to produce a system of environmental performance indicators, called EPIS.

ISO 1440 Lifecycle assessment (LCA) SC5

The first draft appeared in 1995, under the title *General principles and practices.* It will be published in early 1996. This committee is also working on impact assessment and improvement assessment subjects.

Terms and definitions (T & D) SC6
The first draft, *Draft guide on terminology*, was published in June 1995.

The alignment of ISO 9000 – ISO 14000

In Chapter 4 we looked at the relationship between ISO 9000 and ISO 14000, and by 1995 joint meetings of TC 207 and TC 176 had produced a three-phased plan for the alignment of ISO 9000 and ISO 14000. Here it is in summary once again.

1. Short-term goal – compatibility between ISO 9000: 1994 (Phase One) and ISO 14000: 1995 series of documents.
2. Medium-term goal – compatibility between ISO 9000: 1999 (Phase Two) and ISO 14000: 1995.
3. Long-term goal – harmonization of all standards between the two TCs.

Health and safety

This surfaced as an issue in some of the work of the TCs. The decision taken was to write to the Technical Management Board (TMB) of ISO suggesting that it investigate whether occupational health and safety should be considered for international standardization, and if so which TC should deal with it.

What is new in ISO 14000?

For anyone familiar with BS 7750, here are a few points which reflect differences in emphases more than changes from BS 7750 in ISO 14000:

- There should be a strategic environmental plan – a kind of formal presentation every five to seven years.
- The EMP can include priorities, options, cost/benefit identification of relationships, reviews and assessments.
- Contractors on site are mentioned.
- Emergency planning and response is included.
- The environment management manual is stressed.
- A more formal internal reporting system is required. This can be achieved by the EMP review team reporting, perhaps quarterly, to the chief executive officer and publishing a quarterly employee newsletter. There is a report

outline on page 46 of the standard, but it can also be by e mail, bulletin board or newsletter.
- Measuring and monitoring asked for.
- Audit frequencies are left open, and auditors can be internal or external.
- Reviews of the whole system should be carried out at appropriate intervals, and should include performance, suitability of system legislation, changes in demand/product/activities advances in technology, lessons learned.
- Continual improvement is stressed and suggestions made.

Appendix C can be used as an initial review questionnaire. Appendix D suggests an overall phased plan.

Codes of practice

In Chapter 3, we dealt with the helpful ISO 9000 codes of practice which allow you to customize a generic standard to your industry. Now codes of practice for the environmental management standard ISO 14000 are also beginning to emerge. Here is a short list:

Industry/sector	*Title*
Print and packaging	*BSI BS 7750 Sector Application for Print and Packaging*
Transport and distribution services	*BS 7750 Sector Application Guide for Transport and Distribution Services* published by the UK Road Haulage Association
Waste management	*Guidance Notes for the applicability of BS 7750 to Waste Management* published by the UK Institute of Wastes Management

Note that transport and distribution codes exist for both quality and environment, making it particularly easy for that industry to implement ISO 9000/ISO 14000.

7

Initial Environmental Review (IER)

The title of this chapter is called in BS 7750 'the Preliminary Environmental Review', or PER; in ISO 14000 it is called 'the Initial Environmental Review'. As its name suggests, this is a once-off exercise at the beginning of a project.

The format proposed in this chapter could also be used as a means of examining the environmental effects of new projects, without using the references to past experiences. The first step will be the securing of management commitment to implement an environmental management system to the requirements of the ISO 14000 standard. The second will be to carry out the IER. It may also be practical to build the Register of Regulations at the same time as carrying out the IER. Throughout the project one will find that a number of steps are best done in parallel as they compliment each other, one providing information for the other.

What ISO 14000 asks for

After obtaining senior management commitment, the draft ISO 14000 has a paragraph on the IER (Para 4.1.3), suggesting the following:

- Identification of legislative requirements.
- Identification of environmental aspects, significant impacts and liabilities.
- Evaluation and documentation of significant environmental issues.
- Assessment of performance compared to relevant internal criteria, external standards, regulations, codes of practice and sets of principles.
- Existing environmental management practices and procedures.
- Identification of the policies and procedures dealing with procurement and contracting activities.
- Feedback from the investigation of previous incidents of non-compliance.
- Opportunities for competitive advantage.

Commentary

First, there is as yet no required formal structure for the IER although one is suggested shortly, which has worked well in some of the first companies to be certified.

The legislative requirements will be in the Register of Regulations. The actual list of statutory instruments can be shown in the IER if one wishes to do so.

Environmental aspects and significant impacts will emerge from the review. 'Liabilities' is a peculiar word in the draft, as many companies will want to view these as necessary trade-offs for some vital product manufactured such as food or drugs. The text may have intended to address activities with a potential for bad public relations.

The full evaluation and documentation of significant environmental issues cannot be done in the IER as these will be complete only when all the documentation is completed.

While some initial assessment of performance compared to relevant internal criteria, external standards, regulations, codes of practice and sets of principles may be carried out at the IER stage, this also will be complete only when all the documentation is completed; however, the paragraph is a good reminder that policy, codes of practice and standards will also form targets to be met, and not just the compulsory legislation. An example of a set of principles and a code of practice is the chemical industry's RCP.

Existing environmental management practices and procedures will be reviewed in the IER, warts and all, and the more honest one is about past performance the better one's improvements and intentions will seem.

The identification of the policies and procedures dealing with procurement and contracting activities reminds us that off-site indirect activities, such as those carried on by our suppliers when manufacturing our raw materials and components, may be more significant than our direct-site activities. In addition to suppliers, sub-contractors on- or off-site may contribute to both bad environmental practices and risks to public and staff health and safety. Haulage or transport companies carrying our finished product may also have significant environmental implications.

Feedback from the investigation of previous incidents of non-compliance is formally asked for, first in the IER and later in the EMP, especially in the evaluation of incidents and non-conformances.

Opportunity for competitive advantage is something which will more likely be taken up at the stage when one is submitting a proposal to management to get the commitment to implement the EMS.

In the following outline of the contents of a possible IER, most of what appears relevant in the above list is catered for. The reader should remember that, by its nature, an IER cannot give a complete picture. Too much time spent on it will delay implementation of the EMS.

In addition to the above list, the standard asks that consideration be given to the possibility of incidents and emergencies in the IER. This is dealt with in this book in the later health and safety documentation. It finally asks that the IER be documented, and that it identify 'further opportunities for EMS development', a strange request seeing that it is the initial step in a process which is going to achieve just that.

General outline of the IER

The contents of the IER as listed below, and as described in the following sections, may be sufficient for more experienced readers. For the less experienced reader, packages of generic documentation, including sample IERs, are available from Gower.

1.0 Site history, location and use.
2.0 Manufacturing processes described.
3.0 Where we stand now environmentally.
  3.1 Past and present performance.
  3.2 Other standards employed.
  3.3 Work under way.
4.0 Legislative situation.
  4.1 Our knowledge of the situation.
  4.2 The actual regulations.

5.0 Operations.
- 5.1 Goods inward.
- 5.2 Storage.
- 5.3 In-process handling.
- 5.4 Goods out.

6.0 The apparent issues.
- 6.1 The general issues.
- 6.2 Our site specific operational issues.

7.0 Materials usage.
- 7.1 Main production.
- 7.2 Office.
- 7.3 Other.

8.0 Energy usage.
- 8.1 Electricity.
- 8.2 Oil.
- 8.3 Other.

9.0 Supplier considerations.

10.0 Policy.
- 10.1 Policy statement.
- 10.2 Objectives and targets.
- 10.3 Environmental management system.

11.0 Emergency response.

12.0 The actions planned.
- 12.1 Once-off issues to be dealt with after the IER.
- 12.2 Issues which will be controlled under the EMS.
- 12.3 The targets and objectives.

Appendix 1 Lists of substances employed.
Appendix 2 Legal issue questionnaire.
Appendix 3 Supplier questionnaire.

1.0 Site history, location and use

This is routine information, but the material used here can be repeated in an almost similar paragraph of the Environmental Management Manual (see Appendix 2). The site is the facility implementing the system. A site-by-site system will be required with separate inspections and certifications for each where there are multiple sites.

2.0 Manufacturing processes described

This is also routine information, with the material used here also repeated in the Environmental Management Manual.

3.0 Where we stand now environmentally

One can be quite critical about past and even present performance as success is seen to be achieving improvement. A minimum requirement when looking for a reasonable starting benchmark can be that the requirements of the law are being met. After that, environmental targets can be set.

Oil spills, debris on the site, leaking valves, emissions, discharges, fires, accidents can all figure here.

Other standards employed can be ISO 9000 or industry codes of practice. Work under way can be ISO 14000 or an industry code of practice.

4.0 Legislative situation

The most important comment will be about the company's past and recent awareness of the situation. Does management actually know the law? At this stage the process of compiling a list and copies of the actual regulations will be under way for the Register of Regulations. The list can be included here. One may not, however, know the complete list until the system is almost implemented for reasons which will be clearer as we go through the EMP and in particular the effects evaluation procedure.

5.0 Operations

This is a straightforward description of operations such as Goods inward, Storage, In-process handling, Goods out. Service companies should adapt accordingly.

6.0 The apparent issues

This is a useful way to approach the issues in two steps – first all the obvious ones we know about, such as emissions, discharges, waste, and then some not so obvious. The general issues which apply to most companies can be listed first. These are:

- Emissions to the air.
- Discharges to water resources.
- Water supplies and sewage treatment.
- Waste.
- Nuisances.
- Noise.
- Odours.
- Radiation.
- Amenity, trees and wildlife.
- Urban renewal.
- Physical planning.
- Environmental impact assessment.

- Product disposal.
- Packaging.
- Materials use.
- Energy use.
- Product use.
- Process/public safety.
- Staff health and safety.
- Integrated pollution control directive (for certain EU industries).

These general issues could be followed by such a comment as: Unless our investigations prove otherwise, the following general issues should not be relevant to our site:

- Sewage treatment.
- Radiation.
- Urban renewal.

After the general issues, the site or operational specific issues can be listed, such as:

- Effluent/water quality.
- Air emissions/odour.
- Noise.
- Waste.
- Groundwater.
- Fireponds.
- Emergency response.
- Waste minimization.
- Energy conservation.
- Environmental probity of raw materials.
- Environmental probity of suppliers' activities.
- Transport.

Also at this stage known once-off issues can be listed:

- Exposure to acid vapours.
- Exposure to solvent vapours.
- Risk of fire.
- Control of partly-filled raw material drums.
- Storage of empty raw material drums.
- Builders' rubble.

- Evidence of past spillages.
- Need for some landscaping.
- Leaking valve on oil tank.
- An accumulation of debris on the site.
- Dumping of pallets.
- Dumping of waste paper.
- Dumping of cardboard.
- Dumping of soiled paper wipes.
- Wasteful water usage.
- Noise.
- Contaminated land.

7.0 Materials usage

Raw materials may be such a significant issue that it will be dealt with separately. In addition to raw materials, we need a programme for reducing the use of in-house materials.

All known materials used can be listed here from copy paper to laser cartridges. Workshop and laboratory materials should not be ignored. Water may be a significant material.

8.0 Energy usage

The status of energy usage, or one's knowledge of it, should be given here, together with any plans for energy reduction. Company cars can be included.

9.0 Supplier considerations

Letters to suppliers, and where necessary questionnaires, can be included here, with the latter shown shortly.

10.0 Policy

What follows is a sample policy statement, which will also be in the Environmental Management Manual. It is biased towards a chemical or process company but other trades or companies can simply drop the reference to the RCP.

POLICY STATEMENT

It is the policy of COMPANY to operate our Liverpool Yardmouth manufacturing facility to standards which produce products conforming to specified standards of quality, reliability and performance, as laid down in our ISO 9000 system, and to carry out this task in an environmentally friendly manner, on a continuing basis, to the requirements of the Responsible Care Programme, using the environmental management standard ISO 14000, and also the requirements of the EU EMAS Regulation (for EU companies).

The Yardmouth management team will ensure that the proper managerial, technical and administrative controls will operate in order to enable this policy to be maintained. The team will also ensure that a high level of customer satisfaction is maintained.

It is the management policy to ensure that all personnel involved in the company's operations have appropriate training, to ensure that each individual concerned understands the environmental aspects and controls of his/her responsibilities.

It is the responsibility of all COMPANY employees to support and apply those sections of the company environmental policy and procedures which relate to their activities within the plant. They will be trained to initiate corrective actions on environmental matters, issues and concerns where and as appropriate.

In pursuance of this policy, COMPANY will conform to the Environmental Management System specified by ISO 14000 and the EU EMAS Regulation, both of which will be linked with our ISO 9000 system, and in so doing meet also with the requirements of the Responsible Care Programme.

Our policy also embraces our relations with our suppliers, with whom we will promote and implement processes and procedures which will be of mutual benefit and which also promote better environmental practices.

It is COMPANY policy to continually strive to improve environmental performance. Our results, where pertinent, will be made available for public review, except where an unfair advantage could be gained by competitors.

This statement will be inserted into our Environmental Management Manual, cross-referenced as required TO ISO 14000.

This policy decision was made by [Name the manager(s)]
on [date]
who with other relevant management personnel have signed it as follows:

11.0 Emergency response

If a system for incidents and emergencies is not fully in place, this should be admitted at the IER stage and given the most immediate and fullest priority. The approach recommended here is that all issues be managed under ISO 14000, but safety carries such important legal obligations that the health and safety system is addressed separately in the Health and Safety Manual. The emergency response procedures are extensive, so one way to deal with them is to summarize them only in the Health and Safety Manual and write them in detail in SOP #1, Emergency Response Procedures.

12.0 The actions planned

This is a repeat of the findings under the apparent issues, but with the general intentions of what will be done about the issues. The full details of how it will be done will be in the EMP and later documents. The actions planned should be listed under the three headings of:

1. Once-off issues to be dealt with after the IER.
2. Issues which will be controlled under the EMS.
3. The targets and objectives.

Appendix 1 Lists of substances employed
Under such regulations as the handling of dangerous substances and the transport of hazardous wastes, one will find the lists of legislated substances. These can be compared with the actual substances handled in the company, so that one identifies those to be controlled.

Appendix 2 Legal issue questionnaire
Some companies use a checklist of regulations applying within industry sectors to ensure that they know what the legislated issues are. (This is a difficult subject which is raised again in this book, see Chapter 8, The Register of Regulations.)

Appendix 3 Supplier questionnaire
A sample questionnaire is illustrated here (see below and pages following to end of chapter). Individual companies will want to adjust this for their own use, but it essentially covers all those questions you should ask of a supplier to ensure compliance with standards your own company is implementing.

Environmental Questionnaire for Suppliers

Supplier:

Completed by:

Date:

1. Environmental Policy

1.1 Do you have a written policy covering the environmental implications of your activities?

continued opposite

continued

1.2 Do you have specific performance targets relating to the environment? If yes, please specify.
1.3 Are you aware of all existing and impending legislation on environmental matters influencing your business?
1.4 Have you assigned specific responsibilities for environmental management?
1.5 Do you communicate the need for environmental awareness to your staff?

2. Products
2.1 List below all products/ product categories you supply to us:
Products:

2.2 List below the legal requirements, standards or codes of practice, if any, which these products are expected to conform to. (If you don't know, but you will investigate, please let us have your target date.)
Products Requirements

2.3 Do you meet the above requirements?
2.4 Are your products designed to allow recycling or re-use either of the whole product or components?
2.5 Describe how your products should be disposed of:
Product: Method of Disposal:

continued overleaf

continued

3. Safe product use

3.1 Please supply copies of all data sheets concerned with safe staff or environmental use of the products supplied to us, or list same if already supplied. We will assume that there is a data sheet for every one of the products supplied which needs same.

3.2 Where your product may affect our customers please specify end-customer instructions if relevant.

4. Your suppliers

4.1 Have you questioned your suppliers about the environmental probity of materials and components supplied to you which may end up in the products you supply to us?

4.2 In all cases where it is relevant, please let us have both a description of the supplier issue and its potential effects - viz, a substance which may have implications for either pollution or resource wastage, and the steps taken/to be taken.

5. Emergency/contingency plans

5.1 Do you have plans for dealing with emergencies or accidents?

6. Energy sources/use

6.1 Have you an energy conservation programme/initiative in your factory?

7. Emissions/discharges

7.1 Have you identified all sources of emissions to water, to air or land?

8. Waste

8.1 Do you know how much waste you produce and what it contains?

9. Raw Materials

9.1 Have you considered the environmental impact of obtaining and using raw materials?

continued opposite

continued

10. Ozone Depleting Substances

10.1 Are any Class I or Class 11 ozone-depleting substances used in the product or during the manufacture of the product? If yes, please identify the substance, its use and target date for elimination.

10.2 Are any potentially hazardous materials used? If yes, please identify the material. Could these be replaced or used in ways which have a lesser impact on the environment, health and safety?

11. Packaging

11.1 In packaging goods for transportation do you seek to minimize the packaging required?

12. Transport and Distribution

12.1 Have you attempted to reduce the impact of your transport and distribution methods on the environment? If yes, please describe how:

8

The Register of Regulations

The document ISO 14000, under Section 4, paragraph 4.1.4 'Legal Requirements', states that the organization should establish and maintain procedures to identify, have access to and understand all legal and other requirements to which it subscribes, directly applicable to the environmental aspects of its activities, products and services.

The earlier drafts of the document also contained practical help boxes in each section and the one here lists four kinds of regulations, which are those specific to the activity, such as a site-operating permit, those specific to the organization's products and services, those specific to the organization's industry, and general environmental laws. It goes on to say that several sources can be used to identify environmental regulations and its updates.

These sources are:

- All levels of government.
- Industry associations or groups.
- Commercial databases.
- Professional legal services.

In this section of the standard there is an important note:

> To facilitate keeping track of legal requirements, an SME may establish and maintain a legal register of all laws and regulations pertaining to its activities, products and services.

Why just 'SME' is a mystery, as this applies to large and small companies alike. The note does however demonstrate that the company must maintain a Register of Regulations, which is what this chapter is about.

Returning to the advice on sources, this is one of the few sections of the standard with which the author of this book can take issue with its architects. After implementing the environmental management standard in a number of companies across different industries, it became obvious that very little help exists anywhere for a company to identify the relevant legislation.

All four of the sources listed above may be found to be inadequate, even in developed economies. And if these are inadequate in the developed countries, companies outside of them face with ISO 14000 much more severe problems than those they face with ISO 9000.

The need for a register

While ISO 14000 requires a Register of Regulations, there is another pressing need for it. Most of the issues which can be managed under the standard have attached to them compulsory legal requirements, not just market or customer demands, as with most of the motivation for ISO 9000. Every senior manager is faced with a legal requirement to know what laws affect his or her functions within a company, and, in a number of respects, particularly in public safety, product safety, and staff health and safety, the manager could incur through ignorance or neglect both corporate and personal liability.

Difficult though it may be, the task of finding out what the regulations are must be faced.

Only in the European Union will one find some progress towards harmonized legislation, but each EU country still has both EU and local laws. Outside the EU in countries such as the US, Canada and Australia, one may find different legislation for each country, state or province. In addition, in all countries the legislation is constantly being updated and added to.

Readers may be surprised to learn that the company solicitor or lawyer may not be able to fully satisfy this requirement, and a little time spent considering this point may help cast further light on the full meaning of an environmental management system.

The legal question

There is a revolution under way in industry which the legal profession may not be fully aware of. It is that all industrial activity, both manufacturing and services, is increasingly compliance driven. We have already looked at the comparisons between the 'drivers' behind the quality management standard and the new environmental management standard; ISO 14000, and its predecessor BS 7750, are, as we have seen, largely compliance driven, as the environment embraces a number of elements which are required under statutory instruments.

The strength of the new conformance driven interest in environmental management standards is underpinned by the issues which they manage. These are compulsory environmental issues, such as emissions, discharges, noise and odour, staff health and safety regulations, process and public safety, and product safety.

Under the 'voluntary' ISO 9000 quality management standard, three other conformance driven issues can be managed: product liability, consumer information, and misleading advertising.

The problem for the legal profession in increasing its business in this growing market can be summed up in a single statement: *the relevant legislation is issue and task based.* Whether the question is which of the over one hundred pieces of food legislation relate to the activities of a food manufacturer or what laws were broken in a shop floor accident, the answers are as much dependent on the process, component, raw material employed, and task being undertaken, as they are on one's knowledge of the statutory instruments.

The EU EMAS regulation illustrates the relationship between standards and regulations, in that its requirements can be met by the implementation of an environmental management standard, such as BS 7750/ISO 14000, plus public disclosure. Such a management standard in turn is reasonable proof of compliance with the legal requirements of the various issues being controlled, whether these be emissions or the needs of pregnant workers, particularly where the management standard is certified by an independent, accredited, certification agency.

In the case of safety, both worker and public, international best codes of practice may also be employed and controlled under the management system. These in turn are issue and task orientated, such as in the COSHH procedures for handling harmful substances or the chemical industry's RCP.

When something goes wrong, an accident or a major non-compliance, only a scrutiny of issue and task can reveal the extent of the adherence or otherwise to a code of practice and the relevancy of one or more statutory instruments. Examples can be found in such situations as work in confined spaces, hot work, manual handling, personal protective equipment, where several statutory instruments could be relevant. For either plaintiff and defendant, knowledge of both issue and task are of paramount importance, as these lead in turn to statutory instrument, documented procedure and codes of practice employed.

Industry is finding that it cannot get support from the legal profession in the construction of the first basic document in the environmental management system, which is the Register of Regulations, as the legal people cannot know all the raw materials and shop floor issues involved. Does a food manufacturer, for example, impose requirements on suppliers back to the farm? Was the incident pulley or fork lift truck related, was it covered by the general requirements of the Factories Act or by a specific health and safety regulation, or did it involve a listed substance?

More importantly perhaps, were the appropriate procedures written, and the training and controls in place, and were these certified by 'accredited' third parties, where either or both certification and accreditation were relevant?

The few consultants already trying to service sophisticated manufacturers in their implementation of environmental management and health and safety systems, are getting new business from simply analysing the statutory instruments, producing checklists and delivering written procedures, audits and control documents. What has clearly emerged is that in our new increasingly regulated environment, it is difficult for companies to know the law.

This is a new market niche which suggests that co-operation is needed between the legal profession and specialists in environmental, staff health and safety and public safety standards.

In the advice which follows for the construction of a Register of Regulations, it will be seen that, as is the case for every other part of the EMS project, the approach is issue orientated. What do we do? And once we know what we do, what materials do we procure, how do our products and services affect our customers, and what goes on at our site?

Once we know all these issues, we can then on an issue basis find out what the law is. We do not examine one hundred pieces of planning legislation, from shopping centres to high-rise car parks, but look instead at the specific regulations affecting our planned factory extension.

The legislation which follows is *a sample only*, and should not be taken as completely relevant. What will be relevant and therefore may be helpful is that the process is one in which the issues are largely identified. These should help the reader to find the legislation.

Companies in any one of the member countries of the EU may have to access a number of sources for the legislation. These sources, or their equivalents, will include departments of the environment, government publications offices (HMSO in the UK), and the EC's local office. The EU companies will also find appropriate EU environmental directives in a European Commission (EC) published document mentioned below.

Here now is an example of how you could obtain the legislation in the UK.

For establishing the traditional environmental regulations use one or both of the first two steps in the following list. For EU directives use step three, and for health and safety regulations the fourth step. Finally, for the product, process and public safety issues go through the process in step five.

1. The statutory instruments obtainable from HMSO. Use the issues listed in the following Register of Regulations to find out which of the statutory instruments you need to purchase.
2. Look up the Croner publication *Environmental Management Loose-leaf*, available from Croner, Croner House, London Road, Kingston-upon-Thames, Surrey KT2 6SR. Tel 0181 547 3333 Fax 0181 547 2637.
3. Purchase, or freely access at any EU office, the seven-volume publication, *European Community Environmental Legislation*, available at any EU office for reference, or for sale at less than £100, to establish the EU directives and regulations.
4. From either the HSE (Health and Safety Executive) or EU office, obtain the EU health and safety regulations. For local UK Health and Safety regulations use the HSE.
5. By the Register of Environmental Effects stage (see Chapter 10) in the process outlined in this book, you should have established all of your relevant issues. For the moment the only source available for associating these with the legislation is the company solicitor. Experiences to date have not been good, as solicitors have wanted to present 100 pieces of possible legislation instead of the relevant five, and it is now hoped that industry specific associations will come up with industry specific lists. Health and safety agencies provide very helpful advice and simple to read publications on hazard identification.

We have seen that a simple list of legislation will not meet the demands of the environmental management system.

In the five steps listed above, the most difficult of them is step five – that of identifying the process and product staff and public safety issues which may attract legislation – but if the IER, the effects evaluation of the EMP and hazard analysis (supported also in the Health and Safety Manual) are followed through scrupulously, the relevant issues will emerge.

Comparison of the issues with the legislation to date will complete the investigation.

Creating the Register of Regulations

The approach recommended here is that the Register of Regulations be one or more ring binders in which the statutory instruments are placed – that is, the Acts of Parliament or other pieces of legislation which relate to your activities. These can go in plastic see-through envelopes in the ring binders.

The first set will be the general environmental and processing (safety) regulations, while the second set will be the health and safety regulations. Ahead of these statutory instruments, construct a page of information about each of the issues, stating in general how they relate to the company, and your policy on each. In addition to the actual laws, add codes of practice and policies, such as ISO 14000, the EMAS regulation, ISO 9000, and the RCP.

The legislation should set the lower limits, though our policies may meet even higher levels of performance or eliminate all pollutants in the legislated categories. For example, with an issue such as a certain amount of effluent below a statutory limit or a limit licensed by the local authority, we need to set our own policy limits on the issue and state them here as if they were a regulation (our own). Similarly, if there is an industry code of practice for an issue, making a product to a standard say, we should set this also as our policy, under self-imposed regulation.

The Register of Regulations is a passive device, simply attesting to the fact that we know the regulations, so do not try to turn it into a control document. It will be trouble enough to keep up to date. The controls come in the next documents.

What follows is a list of sample legislation, codes of practice and policies for a company in a typical EU member state. (Note that codes of practice, policies and legislation are all treated equally as requirements.)

- Physical planning.
- EU EMAS regulation.
- EIA.
- Waste.
- Toxic waste.
- Raw materials.
- Transport.
- Packaging.

- Nuisance and noise.
- Handling of dangerous substances.
- Shipping of dangerous substances.
- Trees, amenities, landscape, and wildlife.
- Effluent discharges.
- Emissions.
- Use of materials.
- Use of energy.
- Product quality.
- Public safety.
- Health and safety.
- Raw materials (that is, the legislation relating to them).
- Supplier/including services activities, such as transport (that is, the legislation relating to them).

Samples

To end this chapter here are some typical pages as widely used in industry. The first sample page concerns waste management, the second and third page health and safety regulations, and the fourth page a statutory instrument used as a directive.

COMPANY

Register of regulations | | Page 7 of 21
Normal waste | REV: 000 | Date 02/11/96

Regulations

There are four regulations applicable to our operations.

1. European Communities (Waste) Regulations, 1979 (S.I. No. 390 of 1979).
2. European Communities (Waste) Regulations, 1984 (S.I. No. 108 of 1984).
3. The 4th and Final EC Directive on Packaging Waste.
4. Litter Act No. 11 of 1982.

Policy

There are also principles and policies laid out in the EC document *A Community Strategy for Waste Management* SEC (89) 934 1989. It is our policy to support the principles stated here in our operations, particularly in our housekeeping, in the disposal of our waste material and in the products being sold through our distributors.

The first of the above regulations demands that local authorities be responsible for the provision of waste management in our area. It is our policy to commit all of our waste to the local authority, or to a registered operator, registered under the 1978 regulations. It is our policy to check that all waste disposal operators used by us produce evidence of such registration. For as long as the local authority, or registered operator, continues to manage our waste this policy will apply. In the event of the local authority, or registered operator, not being able to manage our waste, we shall store it safely on site until the local authority resumes management, or until safe and legal alternative management can be arranged.

We will also ensure that our waste is recycled as far as possible.

Reference

Register of Effects - Page 13

Control and Monitoring Manual - Page 8

COMPANY

Register of regulations — Page 3 of 21
Health and safety regulations REV: 000 — Date 02/11/96

Regulations
These are as follows:

- Framework and Safety, Health and Welfare at Work Act
- Workplace
- Work equipment
- Visual display units
- Manual handling
- Personal protective equipment
- Pregnant workers
- Temporary workers
- Safety signs
- Limit Values
- Asbestos worker protection
- Carcinogens
- Biological agents
- Exposure to noise
- First aid
- Electricity
- Notification of accidents and dangerous occurrences

This page would be followed in the manual by policy pages on each of the above itemized subjects. The following sample page shows such for the framework regulations.

COMPANY

Register of regulations — Page 4 of 21
Relevant regulations — REV: 000 — Date 02/11/96

Framework/Safety, Health and Welfare at Work Regulations

Regulations

1. European Communities Directive Framework (89/391/EEC).
2. Safety, Health and Welfare at Work Regulations 1989.
3. Safety, Health and Welfare at Work (General Application) Regulations 1993 (S.I No. 44 of 1993).

Policy

A number of elements are set out for attention in the workplace regulations. All of these are set out in the Health and Safety Manual and the procedures to ensure that they are met are laid down in the Environment Management System. All are filed also in this register in the section which follows.

It is our policy to ensure that all the demands of the regulations are met by us.

In addition to the workplace and the other specific Health and Safety regulations which follow, the Framework directive and the Health, Safety and Welfare at Work Acts set the overall policy and framework for health and safety. It is company policy to conform to these by conforming to the specific regulations here and following.

A separate Safety Policy Statement as required by the 1989 Act has been drawn up. See Health and Safety Manual.

Reference

Health and Safety Manual

We file the actual regulations and directives at the back of the binders in transparent folders. This means producing a fairly hefty register.

COMPANY

Register of regulations Page 00 of 00
Environment relevant regulations REV: 000 Date 25/10/94

STATUTORY INSTRUMENTS
S.I. No. 266 of 1993

AIR POLLUTION ACT, 1992, (LICENSING OF INDUSTRIAL PLANT) REGULATIONS, 1993

(PI.5942)

---

2 [266]

S.I. No. 266 of 1993

AIR POLLUTION ACT, 1992, (LICENSING OF INDUSTRIAL PLANT) REGULATIONS, 1993

The Minister for the Environment, in exercise of the powers conferred on him by sections 10, 30, 31, 33, 34 and 35 of the Air Pollution Act, 1992 (No. 6 of 1992) hereby makes the following Regulations:-

Citation

1. These Regulations may be cited as the Air Pollution Act, 1992 (Licensing of Industrial Plant), Regulations, 1993.

Commencement

2. These Regulations shall come into operation on the 1st day of November, 1993.

9

The Environmental Management Programme (EMP)

The EMP is the totality – the on-going programme which controls the day-to-day EMS (which may be largely automated) together with the initial project including the IER. It encompasses once-off findings, the analyses of all new projects, processes and products for their environmental implications, the team and monthly meetings, the publishing of performance and policy, decisions to adopt various standards and codes of practice, or to meet voluntary regulations such as the EU EMAS regulation, and the setting of objectives and targets.

Other students of the standard may give other interpretations of programme versus system, and neither BS 7750 nor ISO 14000 are clear on the distinction. The author has had to settle for an approach and this was the one chosen for better or worse, and which he has used for implementing the standard in industry. So far it has worked quite well in several of the first companies to have implemented environmental management systems to the requirements of BS 7750/ISO 14000.

This chapter is both a description of the EMP and the steps needed to meet its requirements. It includes a step-by-step programme which can be adopted by the reader and contains specific procedures, documents and systems needed to operate the programme, and as such should constitute an actual EMP.

The first draft of ISO 14000 appears to be more project-oriented than programme-oriented. It has sections such as how to start, define purpose/establish plan, ensure capability, and so on, little of which is of assistance to establish the on-going programme after the EMS is implemented. ISO 14000 and ISO 14001 are similar to ISO 9000 and ISO 9001, in that the 000s are supposed to tell you how to implement a system meeting the standard while the 001s give you a paragraph-by-paragraph methodology which is particularly suitable for obtaining third-part certification. Section 4 of the second two, including its sub-paragraphs actually becomes your quality or environmental management manual, and, as a result, the checklist approach for showing to the certifying inspector. In general both ISO 9000 and ISO 14000 can be regarded as the inspirational documents, as one could not implement a practical system from either of them alone. While ISO 14001 clearly specifies an environmental management programme, it has in a quite extra-ordinary manner relegated this totality to sub-paragraph 4.2.4, with the following text:

> The organization shall establish and maintain a programme for achieving its objectives and targets. It shall include:
> (a) designation of responsibility for achieving targets at each relevant function and level of the organization; and
> (b) the means and time frame by which they are to be achieved.

It goes on as follows:

> If appropriate, programmes shall be amended to ensure that environmental management will also apply to projects relating to new developments, new or modified activities, products and services. The setting of the objectives to be obtained shall be part of these programmes.

The two extracts above provide us with the total programme which manages all the sub-systems. We move now to how to implement it in a practical way.

Creating the Environmental Management Programme

In BS 7750 the BSI describe the EMP as follows:

> Over and above the day-to-day controls which are the on-going part of the programme, the environment manager, assisted by the programme review team shall manage the following.

1.1 An analysis of the actions needed to deal with the environmental consequences of the organization's past activities.
1.2 The management of the environmental issues relating to the development of new products or services – in particular an analysis of the life cycle of each new product.

1. General

To satisfy both this and the requirements of ISO 14000 for the EMP, and to ensure that all other matters demanded under the series are satisfied, we need an environmental management manager, the full system specified in this book, an environmental management review team which meets at least monthly, an agenda (see below: '4. The programme review team'), and a *modus operandi* (see below: '2. The programme'). This is the EMP.

Taking the two points above before moving on to the other requirements of the EMP, the analyses of past activities will be done once with the IER, although the architects of the standard may also mean on-going incidents, which will be dealt with anyway in the system and reviewed by the review team. As for life cycle analyses, BS 7750 did not tell us how to do it, but helpful approaches such as that provided by Proctor and Gamble for print and packaging have since emerged (see Chapter 11). The ISO 14000 team have now provided guidelines for life cycle analyses in ISO 14040 (also discussed in Chapter 11).

Other needs

Other needs of the EMP are that all new product plans will be referred to the environment manager. (This may involve discussions with parent or sister companies about new product design. One needs to specify how this is to be done, who will contact the design source, who will carry out the analysis, using specialist help where necessary.)

Similarly, all planned or new processes will be scrutinized by the environment manager and discussed with the programme review team, using specialist assistance as needed.

All planned or new extensions will be referred to the environment manager, who will liaise with the local authority to ensure appropriate compliancies. The full implications of each development will be examined by the environment manager to establish the effect, if any, on the EMS.

2. The programme

The EMP consists of five parts:

2.1 The once-off issues to be dealt with as a result of the findings of IER.
2.2 The issues to be controlled under the EMS, identified in the development of the IER, the Register of Regulations, and the Register of Effects.
2.3 The objectives and targets.
2.4 The on-going review, updating and management of 2.1, 2.2, and 2.3 above at the monthly meetings.
2.5 New programmes.

BS 7750 specifies that only programmes with significant environmental effects need to be considered.

3. Responsibilities

Commitment from the highest management levels is specified in ISO 14000 and BS 7750 has already established that the chief executive officer has the ultimate responsibility for the programme, advised by and assisted in the matter by the environment manager. The day-to-day running of the programme is carried out by the environment manager.

Paragraph 4.3.2.3 of ISO 14000 asks for responsibility and commensurate authority for the overall effectiveness of the EMS to be assigned to a senior person(s) or function(s) with sufficient independence, qualifications, and resources to exercise the necessary responsibilities. This is a less than practical statement. The system will operate only with a single environment manager in charge. This can be the quality manager also, although process plants may consider that environment/safety must be separate. The paragraph also asks that both line managers and employees at all levels should be accountable within the scope of their responsibilities. What this means is that one needs to know what processes are involved at all levels.

The responsibilities for the programme are carried out as follows:

3.1 By the environment manager and programme review team (see paragraph below).
3.2 By the personnel designated under Responsibilities (see the Environmental Management Manual in Appendix 2).

BS 7750 defines the last requirement as the 'designation of responsibility for targets at each *relevant* function and level of the organization'.

4. The programme review team

After or during the IER, the environment manager should set up a programme review team, as the first step in the EMP. Its purpose is to meet the requirements of ISO 14000, while its *modus operandi* might be described in the documented EMP as follows:

```
In accordance with the requirements of ISO 14000 for the
EMP and for general communications, the company has
established and will maintain procedures for receiving,
documenting and responding to communications. All commu-
nications outside of those which are part of the EMS go
to the environment manager in the first instance who
decides if they signal a non-conformance needing action
and, whether or not they do so, are considered and fur-
ther action, if needed, decided on at the monthly
programme review team meetings. [These could include
calls from outside, incidents, once-offs needing immedi-
ate action.] Separate programmes and targets shall be
developed in respect of the environmental management of
projects relating to new developments.
```

The initial and on-going programme will include:

(a) Designation of responsibility for targets at each level.
(b) Means by which they are to be achieved.

In each case where programmes or controls are specified here, and in the Control and Monitoring Manual (see Chapter 10), the persons responsible are specified.

Means
The means or mechanisms are:

- Effects evaluation procedure (which follows below)
- Register of Effects
- Control and monitoring manual
- SOPs
- Monthly EMP meetings.

The procedures for dealing with proposed changes are the decisions taken and documented at the EMP meetings.

The corrective mechanisms are:

(a) Actions taken by the environment manager, as perceived to be necessary.
(b) Actions following EMP meetings decisions.

Programme review team membership
The structure of the programme review team will be presented as a document which will look something like the following.

Member	Title
Joe Soap	Environmental manager
Mary Scott	Safety officer
John Key	Production manager
Meetings	Monthly on First ( )s at 0.00 am.
Agenda	To be drawn up by environment manager

The agenda will be drawn up to address:

1. The once-off issues to be dealt with as a result of the findings of IER.
2. The day-to-day issues controlled under the EMS, identified in the development of the IER, the Register of Regulations, and the Register of Effects.
3. The objectives and targets.
4. The review, updating and management of 1, 2 and 3 above.
5. New programmes, if any.

Programme review team corrective action
In taking corrective action the team will ensure attention to:
(a) Determine the cause.
(b) Draw up a plan.
(c) Initiate preventative action to a level required by the risks.
(d) Apply controls to ensure effective preventative results.
(e) Record any changes in the procedures resulting from the corrective action.

The initial and on-going programme

In the remainder of this chapter documents and procedures which may be helpful are described. These include some which are amongst the most important in implementing a comprehensive EMS and EMP.

The once-off issues to be dealt with as a result of the findings of the IER are listed below and the means of dealing with them are also shown.

ISSUES	**MEANS**
Exposure to acid vapours	Ventilation
Exposure to solvent vapours	Ventilation
Risk of fire	H&S system
Control of partly-filled raw material drums	Drum control
Storage of empty raw material drums	Drum control
Builders' rubble	Clean up
Evidence of past spillages	Clean up
Need for some landscaping	Clean up
Leaking valve on oil tank	Fix
An accumulation of debris on the site	Clean up
Dumping of pallets	Recycle
Dumping of waste paper	Recycle
Dumping of cardboard	Recycle
Dumping of soiled paper wipes	Waste removal
Wasteful water usage	Minimization programme
Noise	To be studied
Contaminated land	Clean up

Action programme for once-offs

Designation of responsibility for targets at each level will be designed as:

Persons responsible for actions

Name	Action
___-	
___-	
___-	
___-	

Schedule

The schedule for dealing with the once-off IER issues will require simple adding of dates to the copy below.

```
Issue                                   Dealt with by
```

Issues

List here all the day-to-day issues controlled under the EMS: these will include planning, emissions, discharges, and so on.

Limits/controls

These are set for control of the above production-specific issues and require eventual completion of the copy below.

```
Issue                                   Limits/controls
```

It will not be possible to fill in this section until after the exercise of the Effects Evaluation Procedure (which follows below; see next section). The limits can be stated here in detail or this can simply say that the limits are those shown in the Register of Effects and/or the Control and Monitoring Manual, using the following statement:

> All of the above will be controlled under the EMS in accordance with the targets set in the Register of Effects and the mechanisms of the Control and Monitoring Manual.

Objectives and targets

These can be expressed in three statements:

1. The fixing or elimination of all the IER once-off issues, such as site rubble and so on.
2. A set of specific targets, such as improved limits on controlled issues, different raw materials, better transport, more support to suppliers, staff involvement in their communities, a waste minimization programme.
3. A minimum requirement of meeting the daily/weekly targets of the EMS.

Programmes for new developments

For all new developments, separate programmes should be developed with the following main elements:

(a) Details of environmental objectives to be obtained.
(b) Mechanisms for their achievement.
(c) Procedures for dealing with proposed changes.
(d) Corrective mechanisms.
(e) The mechanisms of the main EMP above.

BS 7750 asks that this be done for new developments (products or processes) 'where the modification introduces significantly different environmental effects'.

Effects Evaluation Procedure

The Effects Evaluation Procedure can begin in the IER; indeed the standard appears to expect an unreasonable amount of it to be completed at that early stage. Here it is shown as an integral part of the EMP and should be referenced at the monthly review meetings, if for no other reason than it must be done continuously if new developments, raw materials, components, processes or developments are to be appraised fully. The environment manager is responsible for keeping it up to date. New developments discussed at the review meetings may result in new issues and their effects being incorporated into the Effects Evaluation Procedure. It is intended to meet the requirements of the standard and is used also as the basis for information for the Register of Effects, the control and monitoring procedure and the objectives and targets.

Stages in the evaluation

The main purpose of the Effects Evaluation Procedure is to establish a list of issues which may require control or other action and then to assess the significant effect of such control or action, whether direct or indirect. The latter may encompass both supplier and customer activities. The stages of the evaluation are as follows:

Stage 1. Draw up a list of overall potential effects EAP #1.
Stage 2. Carry out an analysis of effects EAP #2.
Stage 3. Identify significant environmental effects EAP #3.
Stage 4. Devise measures.

List of overall potential effects EAP #1

- Physical planning.
- Waste.
- Toxic waste.
- Raw materials.
- Transport.
- Packaging.
- Nuisance and noise.
- Handling of dangerous substances.
- Shipping of dangerous substances.
- Trees, amenities, landscape, and wildlife.
- Effluent discharges.
- Emissions.
- Use of materials.
- Use of energy.
- Product quality.
- Raw materials.
- Public safety.
- Health and safety.

Analysis of effects EAP #2

The effects of the EAP will be presented in a manner suitable for analysis by the team and will look something like the table at the top of the page opposite.

Issue	Pollution	Resource usage	Indirect /Direct
Physical planning			D
Waste		X	D
Toxic waste	X		I
Raw materials	X	X	I
Transport	X	X	I
Packaging	X	X	I
Nuisance and noise	X		D
Trees, amenities, landscape, and wildlife	X		D
Effluent discharges	X		D
Emissions	X		D
Use of materials		X	D
Use of energy	X	X	D
Product quality	X	X	I
Handling of dangerous substances			D
Shipping of dangerous substances			I
Process/public safety			D
Health and safety [dealt with in H&S system]			D

Significant environmental effects EAP #3

Issue	Pollution	Resource usage	Indirect /Direct
Emissions	X		D
Effluent discharges	X		D
Noise	X		D
Toxic waste	X		I
Other waste	X	X	D
Raw materials	X	X	I
Transport	X	X	I
Packaging	X	X	I
Use of materials (internal)		X	D
Use of energy	X	X	D
Product safety			D

Certain of the direct issues such as effluent discharges, emissions, waste and the use of undesirable substances, could also be indirect if they occur in the processes of suppliers or in use by customers. Raw materials can be handled under the supplier management programme. Waste can also occur or be dealt with under Packaging. The controls used for all of these can be in the Control and Monitoring Manual.

Measures

These will be employed as follows:

ISSUE	MEASURE
Emissions	See emission control procedure
Effluent discharges	See effluent control procedure
Noise	See noise control procedure
Toxic waste	See waste control procedures
Other waste	See waste control procedure
Raw materials	Supplied component/materials effects evaluation
Transport	Supplied component effects evaluation
Packaging	Direct - product design Indirect - supplied component effects evaluation
Use of materials	Direct - materials minimization programme: Indirect - supplied component effects evaluation
Use of energy	Energy conservation programme
Product safety	See Product safety manual or data sheets

An important point is that some of the significant issues may be in the hands of suppliers. The company must demand evidence that these are being controlled by the supplier. The means employed are the supplier questionnaire and the Supplied Component/Materials Effects Evaluation Procedure (a supplier could also be the transporter of finished product), as:

```
Supplied Component/Materials Effects Evaluation -
Product/component/material
Name the item viz, a specific raw material substance.
Supplier:   XYZ Corp
```

The above document requires a format which provides details of the raw material or component, its environmental attributes, and the needed controls. Do not hesitate to demand this from suppliers. This is a very important point as many companies will find that the significant issues are supplier related, but the standard expects companies to take responsibility for all materials acquired. Each company must analyse its own supplied raw materials, and there could be dozens of such analyses for each component/material. Only established significant issues need be analysed thus, and the purpose is to identify the issue so that the supplier can be asked to co-operate by providing certificates of compliance to the decided acceptance levels. Where significant issues are so identified telephone calls or specific letters to the supplier can complement or take the place of the supplier questionnaire. The reason for this is that a few issues may be so significant that they warrant a partnership type approach with the supplier. The latter may in turn have to go up the supply chain to earlier stages or primary source of supply. A good example is the obtaining of timber for print and packaging only from managed forests.

Summary

Where do we now stand regarding the EMP and its implementation?

1. The IER has established the apparent issues to be controlled.
2. From the Register of Regulations we know the law concerning our issues and we have also stated available codes of practice and our policies on these and other issues.
3. The EMP is both a structure for implementing the programme and managing it.
4. The Supplied Component/Materials Effects Evaluation Procedure is a 'live' working document, part of the EMP, which allows us to discover the significant supplier issues in the first instance, and then allows periodic analyses of same, particularly if new materials are procured. It complements the supplier letter and questionnaire.
5. We are now in a position to generate the Register of Effects and the Control and Monitoring Manual.

10

Register of Environmental Effects and Control and Monitoring Manual

As the first drafts of ISO 14000 circulated, the certification agencies were being accredited by agencies like the NACCB to audit companies to standards such as BS 7750. The backlash against using checklists for certification to ISO 9000 was already under way, and the agencies were being informed that their accreditation required them to ensure that the environmental management standard dealt with real or significant issues.

A good way to explain the thinking behind this is to imagine the European manufacturing facility of a leading world software company. It has one European site, at which there are very few apparent issues. There are no emissions or discharges of any consequence, waste is of a nature that can be recycled and the company could find itself concentrating on trivial issues such as a reduction in the use of office copy paper and the planting of shrubs on site. The inspector calls and asks where are the controls for the 50,000 trees each year which go into the production of its computer manuals and what about the transport of products all over Europe.

In concentrating on the direct site issues, the company could miss the major issues because they are indirect.

The Register of Effects

The formula for examining the effects of the issues is to employ four simple headings:

1. Direct.
2. Indirect.
3. Resource using.
4. Pollution.

Understanding the words used is very important. The whole system is based on the identification of the issues. These are planning, emissions, discharges, noise, waste, process safety, raw materials and so on. There could be five or six general waste categories: normal to landfill, toxic, oil, glass, paper, board, and pallets. The system identifies, measures and controls the effects of the issues. In a chemical plant there could be a dozen possible effects of the single issue of emissions, and the same for water-based discharges. With noise there may only be one potential bad effect, which is a decibel level over a set threshold at the plant's fence line. An effect of paper made from pulp from mills buying from non-managed forests could be the destruction of the forests.

ISO 14000 is not strong with emphases on issues and effects, using such expressions as 'aspects' and 'impacts'. In what may be a Canadian way of saying things, paragraph 4.2.2 is entitled 'Identification of Environmental Aspects and Evaluation of Associated Environmental Impacts', which is difficult to interpret. The paragraph goes on to say that the identification of the environmental aspects is

> an on-going process that determines the past, current and potential impact (positive or negative) of an organization's activities on the environment. This process also includes the identification of the impact to the health and safety of people and the potential regulatory, legal and business exposure affecting the organization. It can also include risk assessment.

It is a pity that while the health and safety of people is recognized here that the authors of ISO 14000 still see staff health and safety as optional, and few process companies would not include risk assessment. Perhaps later drafts of paragraph 4.2.2 will change 'Identification of Environmental Aspects and Evaluation of Associated Environmental Impacts' to 'Identification of the issues and their effects'.

In ISO 14001 where one expects the details, under the paragraph 'Environmental aspects', little more is added. It says:

> The organization shall establish and maintain a procedure to identify the environmental aspects of its activities, products, and services that it can control and over which it can be expected to have an influence, in order to determine those which have or can have significant impacts on the environment.

Let us try to rewrite this as follows.

> The organization should implement a system to identify and manage the issues which have significant, or potentially significant, implications for the environment. To achieve this both direct and indirect issues and their effects should be considered from both the pollution and resource usage points of view.

Perhaps what is most remarkable about both ISO 14000 and ISO 14001 is how little they say about this fundamental matter of establishing effects. The kind of Register of Effects proposed here does not seem to exist, but it would be very difficult to manage a practical system without one.

Several proposed sample pages for a Register of Effects now follow.

They are needed in the first instance for all of the significant issues – and they should be followed by a similar page for all the issues chosen for control. Note that these sample pages cover direct and indirect issues, pollution and resource usage.

Doc. No: RE-01	COMPANY	Date of Issue: 01.01.97
	Register of Effects	
Approved by:		Page No 6 of 24

Issue: Transport				
Effects				
	Pollution	Significance	**Resource Usage**	Significance
Direct	There is a small number of COMPANY company cars for managers. The cars are fitted with catalytic converters.	low	Use of fossil fuels	low
Indirect	As COMPANY is a big user of transport in the delivery of product, pollution could arise from the uncontrolled use of transport. This is a major indirect supplier issue. The main effects are pollution, with vehicle emissions of CO^2, nitrogen oxides, hydrocarbons, carbon monoxide and lead.	high	There are also high resource usage effects, with use of fossil fuels, vehicles, tyres, and so on.	high

Elements needing control	**Controls**
Routing Emissions Fuel consumption Tyre usage Resources Documentation Video conferencing	Backloading Lead free fuel Impose speed limit Monitor tyre usage Recondition rather than replace Use EDI/other electronic messaging All of these are to be addressed in a new transport programme with suppliers.

Doc. No: RE-01	COMPANY	Date of Issue: 01.01.97
	Register of Effects	
Approved by:		Page No 7 of 24

Issue: Raw materials			**Component**: (list)	
Effects				
	Pollution	Significance	**Resource Usage**	Significance
Direct	There are no apparent direct polluting effects other than our processing issues already dealt with. All the quality and safety checks are carried out under our ISO 9000 controls.	none	As we are operating an efficient production system under ISO 9000 controls direct wastage is at a minimum.	low
Indirect	Our suppliers are being asked to inform us of any undesirable processing activities which can be avoided.	not known	We have asked our suppliers about the efficiency of their resource usage.	low
Elements needing control			**Controls**	
			Appropriate certificate See Control and Monitoring Manual	

Issue: Waste water discharges				
		Effects		
	Pollution	Significance	**Resource Usage**	Significance
Direct	Most of the substances discharged can have a detrimental effect on the waters discharged to if the licensed limits are exceeded.	high	None	none
Indirect	There should be none as any significant pollution issue will be direct.	none	None	none
Elements needing control			**Controls**	
We discharge waste effluent into the Park estuary under licence limits. Our limits are 50m3/hour over 24 hours.			Local Authority Licence No. W81 Daily effluent monitoring log DEM1	

Issue: Noise (fenceline)				
		Effects		
	Pollution	Significance	**Resource Usage**	Significance
Direct	Noise levels can have a detrimental effect on staff within the plant and on people in the local community. We operate well within these limits.	high	No significant resource usage.	low
Indirect	There should be none as any significant noise issue will be direct.	none	None	none
Elements needing control			**Controls**	
dBA levels			See Control and Monitoring Manual	

Issue: General waste				
Effects				
	Pollution	Significance	**Resource Usage**	Significance
Direct	As we strictly segregate general from toxic waste, and employ substantial recycling, there is only a small landfill consideration here. We use registered waste disposal operators.	low	We employ a materials minimisation programme which reduces both materials used and their waste output.	low
Indirect	There should be none as any significant pollution issue would be direct.	none	Our materials minimisation programme has the effects of reducing materials bought from suppliers.	none

Elements needing control	**Controls**
Use of authorised licensed operator Materials minimisation programme	See Control and Monitoring Manual

This is what has now been achieved. The IER and Register of Regulations state the passive position, saying this is the law and our policies, and this is as close or as far as we are from this. The EMP puts in place the overall programme, team and procedure, and includes an in-depth scrutiny of issues and their effects, including those of supplied components and other activities of suppliers. The Register of Effects establishes exactly what the effects and potential effects of the issues are. The obvious next steps are control and monitoring, the construction of the top-level Environmental Management Manual (the quality manual of the system), and ensuring that all the SOPs and the Health and Safety systems are in place. Finally, before the certification inspection, a training course must be devised or secured as staff training must commence.

The Control and Monitoring Manual

This can be virtually automated, and in most process industries many of the most fundamental controls will be operated by programmable light controllers and support computers. In deciding whether one needs the kinds of control sheets in ring binders shown here, a simple question can be asked. If you are responsible for a critical function and you want to both make sure that controls are in place and demonstrate this to third parties such as certification inspectors, and in particular be able to produce evidence of such control in the event of an unjustified charge of negligence, would it be better if you had employed dated signed-off documents?

This is the approach recommended here. At the same time do not make it too bureaucratic.

Samples of typical pages from a Control and Monitoring Manual follow.

Local Authority Planning Permission Compliance

Project name/description:		
Architect name: *(Attach to this document letter from architect/project co-ordinator stating that he/she holds full copy of Building Regulations and other relevant planning regulations (such as EIA)and stating what certificates/documents from the local authority will demonstrate compliance with same at end of, and, if necessary stages of, the project. Those local authority certifications must be attached to this document also.)*		
Document required:	**Date received:**	**Signed (by Environment Manager):**
Architect/co-ordinator letter:		
Local authority certification:		
Check only as new projects arise	**Date:**	

Effluent Discharges and Licence Limits

Volume discharge licence limit:	50m3/hour over 24 hours
Target limit:	See daily monitoring record - reference
Name of local authority:	Liverpool Borough
Licence number:	W81

Period licensed

(Attach copy of licence to this document)

Licence inspected:	**Date:**	**Signed (by Environment Manager):**
Daily monitoring record checked:	**Date:**	**Signed:**

Check daily/weekly for monitoring, annually for licence.
Date:

Supplier Compliance Statement

Any new significant issue arising from a supplied material or component will be controlled thus.

Supplier name:		
Issue:		
Attach supplier statement or certificate to this document		
Certificate/document received:	**Date received:**	**Signed (by Environment Manager):**
Check annually and with each new supplier. **Date:**		

11

Product life cycle assessment

Life cycle analyses or assessment is a frequently heard concept in environmental management but one with little information available about how to carry it out. An exception to this is Proctor and Gamble who have made a good spreadsheet model freely available for examining the product life cycle issues in the print and packaging industries.

The most common description of life cycle analyses is the 'cradle-to-grave' approach. In the language of the EMS this means using the processes within the environmental management programme, in particular the effects evaluation analyses, to establish both direct and indirect issues from pollution and resource usage points of view. This means going upstream through suppliers to forest and farm and downstream to distributor and end user and ultimate disposal of waste product.

Up to now no standard has existed for carrying this out, and none is yet required in ISO 14000 or BS 7750, but a series of product life cycle analyses standards are now emerging from a TC 207 sub-committee, the first of which is titled *Committee Draft ISO/CD 14040, Life cycle assessment – General principles and practices.*

Three more standards are under preparation, and these are:

1. ISO 14041: Life cycle assessment – life cycle inventory analysis.
2. ISO 14042: Life cycle assessment – life cycle impact assessment.
3. ISO 14043: Life cycle assessment – life cycle improvement.

What now follows is a commentary on the contents and potential usefulness of the first draft standard on life cycle assessment – ISO/CD 14040.

ISO/CD 14040

The introduction goes straight to the business of understanding and reducing the impact of the 'upstream' and 'downstream' effects of industry, what are described as 'indirect effects' in the system proposed in this book. Life cycle assessment (LCA) is seen in this cradle-to-grave context and not just in site or production activities.

The LCA can be carried out at the design stage when all the potential environmental effects can be evaluated, or at any stage, by identifying all steps in a product development process, such as from farm to trash bin, identifying the inputs to and outputs from each stage, in terms of the use of resources or undesirable releases, and the study of possible alternatives. The standard sees cradle-to-grave as a continuum, along which an LCA can evaluate its environmental impacts, from raw materials acquisition to production, use, and disposal, in terms of traditional environmental impacts, both pollution and resource depletion, and health and safety, although the last is not stressed.

The identification of possibilities for environmental improvement is seen to be the main purpose of the LCA. This process in turn could lead to product re-design, different raw materials, changes in processes, better user instructions, or eco labelling. There is a coming standard and an EU directive on eco labelling. The process works through obtaining environmental information which can help in design and decision-making processes.

As is the case with much of ISO's work, the new standard is also seen as a device for educating both state and private policy makers about the concept, in particular to get across the message that environmental management goes beyond the site, and must be integrated into the corporate policy and overall decision-making process.

The architects of the LCA standard recognize both its newness and limitations, and early implementers should be aware that formal life cycle analyses to the requirements of the standard may not be needed for certification purposes for some time to come. As with all such standards, however, some paragraphs about one's commitment to its principles in the environmental management manual may help to demonstrate one's greater commitment to continuous improvement.

Because of limitations in our abilities to measure qualitative issues and possible trade-offs or counteractions (for example, should we scrap the container and let the food spoil or the rodents in?), the architects warn that the LCA exercise may not be 'a purely objective scientific endeavour' and should be used carefully and appropriately. They go even further and admit that LCA is only one of several environmental techniques and 'may not always be the appropriate tool to use in all situations'.

Central to the standard, and probably its highlight, is a methodology for carrying out a life cycle assessment.

Broadly this covers the following elements:

1. Definition of what you want to measure and its scope.
2. The system, data, calculations and interpretations. (See comments on benchmarking below.)
3. The impact assessment.
4. Assessment of improvement possibilities.

Benchmarking

In the standard, although benchmarking is hinted at in paragraphs about system boundaries and in another paragraph entitled 'Potential user groups' (which is then left hanging in the air), no mention is made. One would think benchmarking to be fundamental to practical life cycle assessment.

Other books deal with this subject (see *The Truth About Outsourcing*, published by Gower), but as the product or process is often the key to benchmarking one would think that benchmarking itself would be a key way of carrying out an LCA.

It is possible that the brief mention of 'potential user groups' in the standard is an indication that the architects see merit in companies not having to reinvent the wheel but be able to develop industry wide benchmarks through industry associations. The most practical way to benchmark against either potential partner companies or competitors is to do it by process or product.

The author took the methodology proposed in ISO 14040 shown above and attempted to cross-reference it to his own proposed methodology for using benchmarking in an outsourcing decision, and the result was as follows:

ISO 14040 – Definition of what you want to measure and its scope

The benchmarking methodology is to decide on the benchmark, as:

- A suitable company already carrying out LCA.
- A product.
- A process.
- All the above.

ISO 14040 – The system, data, calculations and interpretations
The benchmarking methodology is to:

- Assign responsibility to a project leader or consultant.
- Carry out the analysis.
- Visit the benchmark if you have permission or begin the comparisons.
- Analyse the data, in particular looking for differences in performance, seeking both inhibiting and facilitating practices.

ISO 14040 - The impact assessment and assessment of improvement possibilities
The benchmarking methodology is to:

- Use the knowledge of the inhibiting and facilitating practices to amend your own process or make recommendations to management.

Summary

In summary, the approach using benchmarking is to select the product or process for LCA (which is the beginning of the ISO 14040 methodology). Select a company or companies with similar product or processes. Once you have permission or know the legalities of what you propose to do (see the Gower book mentioned above for this subject), go through the methodology outlined above, together with the detailed steps in ISO 14040.

Do not pioneer such a potentially huge investigation when it can be shared with others, unless you have the resources and the will to be an industry leader in the matter.

12

Auditing the systems

While both ISO 9000 and ISO 14000 have auditing sections, spelling out the requirements for the audit of quality and environmental standards, there is also an ISO 10000 series of standards for auditing quality management systems. This can be a little confusing, and is made more so by the fact that while ISO 9000 says a certain amount about auditing and leaves the details to ISO 10000, ISO 14000 has published a number of auditing standards and has plans for more. The rule is to use ISO 10000 to audit ISO 9000 systems, and use the specific ISO 14000 audit series to audit ISO 14000 systems.

The ISO 10000 series

The main standards here are:

- ISO 10011-1 Guidelines for auditing quality systems Part 1: Auditing.
- ISO 10011-2 Guidelines for auditing quality systems Part 2: Qualification criteria for quality systems auditors.
- ISO 10011-3 Guidelines for auditing quality systems Part 3: Management of audit programmes.

Comparing these three with three complimentary ISO 14000 standards we have:

- ISO/CD 14010 Guidelines for environmental auditing – General principles of environmental auditing as the environmental version of the first.
- ISO/CD 14011/1 Guidelines for environmental auditing. Audit procedures – Part 1: Auditing of environmental management systems as the environmental version of the third.
- ISO/CD 14012 Guidelines for environmental auditing – Qualification criteria for environmental auditors as the environmental version of the second.

All three of these environmental standards are dealt with later in this chapter. In addition to the three main ISO 10000 standards above there are:

- ISO 10012–1 and ISO 10012–2 for measuring equipment and measurement process control.
- ISO 10013, which is a guide to the development of quality manuals.

What ISO 9000 demands

ISO 9004 asks for audits on a planned and formal basis, and both ISO 9001 and 9002 repeat this briefly. The 10000 series tells us how to do it, starting with ISO 100011–1.

ISO 10011–1 Guidelines for auditing

The main elements of this standard are:

- Scope and objectives.
- Organization.
- The audit.
- Follow up.

There is no need to take the reader through each of these elements as they are self-explanatory; a look at the standard will give the details, and this is little more than an overview.

The purpose is to see how well the quality management system conforms to its own targets, including both stated customer expectations and requirements imposed on suppliers. Auditors should not have responsibility for sections audited, and the company can develop its own audit format, but a formal approach is required.

ISO 10011–2 Qualification criteria for quality systems auditors

A reading of this interesting document may convince people that it is impossible to be the first auditor anywhere, unless God is in the chair of an evaluation panel deciding who is qualified.

Two things are needed: first, at least second-level education; and, second, that the 'evaluation panel' judges the candidate to be qualified to audit the system.

The evaluation panel can be set up inside or outside the organization. The panel may ask that the candidate be evaluated by an external certification body. The candidate should have four years industrial experience including two years at quality assurance.

A lead auditor is also required who will be in overall charge of the audit. He/she should have been a qualified auditor as above in at least three audits which were in accordance with ISO 10011–1, and should have a proven ability to communicate orally and in writing.

All this is fine for countries mature in ISO 9000 development, with ISO 10000 procedures in place and young auditors who can be brought through such procedures, but how does one begin such a chicken and egg procedure? If the reader is a mature manager with experience of three audits, and is comfortable with the whole subject he or she should declare his or her self to be a lead auditor, setting up their own evaluation panel if necessary. The author is strongly opposed to the idea of cartels of so-called experts creating further barriers to trade and enterprise which will create closed shops of qualified auditors. The standards and certification schemes on their own are quite capable of setting up such barriers without adding additional auditing ones.

The ISO 14000 auditing standards

Here are the ISO 14000 series draft auditing standards:

- ISO/CD 14010.
- ISO/CD 14011/1.
- ISO/CD 14012.

More standards in this series will be prepared in future.

The three are in a familiar ISO format: the first laying down the general principles and guidelines, the second the way to go about the audit, and the third the qualifications needed by the auditor.

ISO/CD 14010

What is apparent from the beginning with this first in a series of environmental auditing standards, is that environmental auditing is itself going to become an industry as distinct from consultancy and certification.

Requirements for an environmental audit

Apart from the obvious fact that the audit should concern the environmental effects of the company's activities (the standard also uses that unfortunate Canadian word 'aspects' instead of issues or effects), the audit should take place only if there is sufficient information to allow the audit. The actual sentence is italicized in the draft standard obtained from TC207 and reads: 'The subject matter and the party who is responsible for it should be clear and documented', which appears to need translation. The balance of the early paragraph is like a copy of the policy statement asking for adequate resources, and related general sentiments.

The objectives and scope of the audit need to be spelled out before the audit and understood by both auditee and auditor.

While the environment manager may have overall responsibility, even when he or she hires an outside consultant, it is assumed that he or she always has independence from the functions being audited and selects the team to ensure both objectivity and competence (that is, independent of the activities they audit).

ISO 14012 suggests the qualification criteria of auditors who can be from inside or outside the company, but 'should not be accountable to those being audited'.

Apart from another somewhat redundant remark that the auditor should use due professional care, there is the important statement that the auditor operates under the direction of the client.

ISO 14011 is to be used as the methodology or guidelines for carrying out the environmental audit. The text is far from clear on how standardized this should be, saying on the one hand that we need 'documented and well-defined methodologies and systematic procedures' and on the other that different types of environmental audits may require 'different methodologies and procedures'. This is one more instance which reinforces the need for industry benchmarks.

And this is further emphasized by text which asks for criteria, and makes very general statements about these. It is hard to imagine an environmental audit to the requirements of the ISO 14000 series being carried out before implementation of a full EMS to the requirements of ISO 14000.

The criteria are very obvious. They are the limits and targets set in the system and reviewed daily and monthly. The text of ISO 14010 reads more like an IER where we do not yet know the criteria.

The whole section on audit criteria, evidence, findings, assurance and risk in ISO 14010 is full of jargon and most unsatisfying. Here, for example, is a statement about assurance and risk:

> The environmental auditor should consider . . . throughout the audit, the risk of reaching an incorrect finding and the risk of reaching an incorrect conclusion, and should take these risks into account in planning and executing the audit.

And following this is the statement:

> The environmental auditor should obtain sufficient evidence to ensure that significant individual findings or aggregates of small findings, which could affect the audit conclusions, are taken into account.

What do these warnings mean? In the next paragraph there is a clue where the fact of the audit's constraints in time and cost are acknowledged so that it is a sample only resulting in uncertainty, but this is not a sufficient explanation for these warnings.

The author's understanding of the situation is that if an EMS has been fully implemented with documented controls in place, an audit will involve both a desk check of the documented controls (such as signed logs and monitors) and a site inspection, and a review of the monthly progress reports. All audits, quality, financial and environmental are snapshots as well as document reviews. The main purpose is to ensure that there is a real working system on the ground. The remarks about assurance and risk in ISO 14010 read as if the writers had not yet seen a fully implemented environmental management system.

In another extraordinary statement the writers say:

> Evidence should be of such a quality and quantity that competent auditors working independently of each other would reach similar findings from evaluating the same evidence against the same criteria.

So much for their remarks about uncertainty.

A written report containing the audit conclusions is required as the main outcome of the audit, and this should be communicated to the client. In the sample report given below the essential elements asked for are included.

The standard sees three different types of environmental audit. This is, once again, familiar ISO thinking with a corollary in three different types of quality manual where there needs be one only. The standard identifies an environmental management system audit, an environmental statement audit, and a compliance audit. Having complicated things thus, it goes on to say that 'the general principles common to all environmental audits, as contained in this standard, apply to each of these types of audit'. The distinction between audit types depends on the subject matter of each individual audit.

The standard telling us how to do the audit

The title of the standard which tells us how to carry out the audit is the Committee Draft ISO/CD 1400/1, *Guidelines for environmental auditing – audit procedures – part 1: Auditing of environmental management systems.*

The main purpose is to determine how well the environmental management system conforms to the requirements of ISO 14001. Other objectives include the determination of the suitability and effectiveness of the environmental management system; the improvement of the system; and, an 'initial' means of assessing the environmental management system of an organization 'where there is a desire to establish a contractual relationship', in other words external verification as in certification, although whether the writers mean this is not certain. What is certain is that they do mean an initial assessment of potential suppliers. The somewhat scant information in the rest of the standard is routine, covering audit objectives, roles, responsibilities and activities, the use of a lead auditor (more about this below), and the constitution of the audit team.

On this last point, consideration should be given to: the need for qualifications as laid down in ISO 14012; the nature of organization, activity or function being audited (for example, pig farm or power station); and the number of auditors and their skills.

More routine information of doubtful value follows about the responsibilities of the auditor(s), operating under control of the lead auditor. In all almost three pages of text, starting with paragraph 4.2, the 'Roles, responsibilities and activities', can be interpreted as 'one should carry out the audit properly'. The section on initiating the audit gives a methodology of sorts, beginning with a preliminary review of the auditee's environmental management system. This is very similar to the initial desk check carried out by some certification bodies on the documentation in the first instance and before any site visit. The standard here mentions 'the environmental management manual or equivalent'. As in the case of the certification desk check, the audit should not proceed if this reveals that the system documentation provided is inadequate.

Instead of going into detailed commentary on what this standard says about preparing for and carrying out the audit, a sample approach incorporating as much as is practical from it is included at the end of this chapter.

Who is qualified to be an auditor?

The standard attempts to answer this question by means of Committee Draft ISO/CD 14012 *Guidelines for environmental auditing – qualification criteria for environmental auditors.* There are two categories of auditor: lead auditors and auditors.

The standard asks for at least the completion of secondary education. Those with 'a relevant degree', whatever that means, should have a minimum of two years 'appropriate' work experience. What is perhaps most frustrating about this standard in the early years of the environmental management revolution is that unless one understands such expressions as relevant and appropriate, it is impossible to know who may be qualified. If one does get clarification, perhaps no-one can ever qualify, as there is no relevant experience before the first time one does something, especially where it involves a new standard.

Those with only secondary education and 'a degree other than a relevant degree' (philosophy, astronomy?) need a minimum of four years' 'appropriate' experience.

More sensible is the requirement that auditors should have completed both formal training and on-the-job training, either inside the organization or externally. To actually qualify as an auditor, one needs to have worked in a training capacity on the job with experienced people, under the control of a lead auditor, and have been involved in the entire audit process, in at least four audits for a total of at least 20 days.

There are also somewhat normative requirements, 'personal attributes and skills that include, but are not limited to' speaking and writing, diplomacy, tact and 'the ability to listen', maturity, judgement, and others, none of which are really believable, given what we already know about the immaturity and lack of know-how of many young quality and accounting audit trainees.

The most interesting character in the audit regime is the lead auditor. The requirements are to have been an auditor throughout at least three complete audits, extending over at least 15 days, and in another normative demand 'to have demonstrated [to whom?] a thorough understanding and application of those personal attributes and skills necessary to ensure effective and efficient management and leadership of the audit process'.

Auditors are expected to maintain their competence by staying up to date with both environmental management standards and a knowledge of regulations (which, as we have noted elsewhere, is both necessary and very difficult).

In a number of places in the auditing standards the authors refer to language, saying specifically that none of the audit team members should participate 'unsupported' in an audit where they are not able to communicate effectively in the language. On first acquaintance, it could be thought that such statements as this reflected the Canadian origins of the standards – with Quebec implications – but on more careful perusal of the sentences concerned it appears that what the authors were saying was something of a sensitive nature. That is, do not use team members in a country where they do not fully understand the language.

This can hardly mean do not bring in people who do not speak English to audit in an English-speaking market, as no-one anywhere can be doing this. We are left then with the interesting assumption that these warnings are directed at the world's leading certification and auditing companies whose teams are operating all over the world. We know for example that a mere 12 certification companies operate in over 60 countries. Are these warnings directed at them?

Evaluating the auditors

From both previous studies of the implications of the ISO 10000 series of quality auditing standards and an Annexe A to the 14012 standard discussed below, the author of this book has come to the conclusion that behind the vagueness of the information about who decides who is and who is not a qualified auditor is the suggestion that a body of some kind can set up its own evaluation procedures. Annexe A gives advice on evaluating the qualifications of environmental auditors, and here is an attempt to interpret it. You can meet the requirements of ISO 14010 by setting up an 'Evaluation system', which can be internal or external to the function being audited. Its purpose is to evaluate the qualification of environmental auditors.

The evaluation system should be directed by an individual or individuals currently active in managing auditing operations. The evaluation will encompass education, work experience, training and personal attributes, which should support the criteria for qualification laid down in the standard (as discussed above). The process should include some of the following methods: interviews with candidates, written and/or oral assessment or other means; candidates' written work; and discussions with former employers, colleagues and others. This evaluation system may itself be subject to a quality assurance process, but this is not demanded, for now at least.

Outline of an audit programme

This is a somewhat brief outline of the main elements in an audit programme for an individual company, written so that the reader can customize it to his or her own requirements.

1. Audit programme

A statement of general intent and the reason for the audit will be stated as:

1.1 General
This audit programme lays down the annual requirements and procedures for auditing the environmental management system at COMPANY.

1.2 Purpose of audits
(a) To determine if our environmental management activities conform to the environmental management programme, and are implemented effectively.
(b) To check the effectiveness of the environmental management system in fulfilling COMPANY environmental policy.

2. Audit plan/organization

Before the audit begins there will be an audit plan along the lines shown below.

2.1 Audit plan
The audit plan should be shown to management who will have the opportunity to review it and ask for changes. Any dissent should involve the lead auditor in its resolution. All parties must agree to it before the audit proceeds. It is doubtful if such a cumbersome procedure could ever be practical on the ground, as normally two parties only will make these decisions – the lead auditor and the company representative, who will be the environment manager responsible for the EMS, but not responsible for production. The routine proposed in draft 14011/1 would

simply result in no audit ever taking place. It is hoped that future revisions will be a little more practical.

The format suggested in the standard is:

(i) Background.

(ii) Objectives.

(iii) Scope and organization, which will encompass
- identification of the audit team members;
- identification of reference documents;
- identification of the organizational and/or functional units to be audited;
- confidentiality requirements.

(iv) Methodology, including
- the identification of the functions and/or individuals within the organization with significant direct environmental responsibilities;
- identification of high priority aspects of the environmental management system or activities;
- the procedure (see below).

(v) Schedule, of
- the expected time and duration for major audit activities;
- the meetings to be held with management.

(vi) Reports, including
- report format and structure, expected date of issue and distribution of the audit report;
- documentation retention requirements.

(vii) Existing documentation.

2.2 Responsibility

Audits are the responsibility of the environment and safety manager, who is independent of the specific areas/functions being audited, but, to meet fully the need for independence of the auditor, he or she will employ independent third parties, either from inside the company or externally as required. At least one audit annually will be carried out by an outside consultant, in conjunction with the environment manager, and the outside consultant will be responsible for the production of the audit report. (This is a suggestion from the author.)

2.3 Audit team assignments

The assignments of each team member will be itemized so that the function to be audited will be apportioned to a named individual. For each function there is a checklist or methodology as required given to the auditor. This procedure can be adapted as required by the lead auditor during the audits.

2.4 Frequencies

Site inspections will take place monthly, and these will use one independent person, either from inside or outside the company quarterly. Specific areas or issues (such as noise) may be audited separately as required.

More general audits will take place quarterly, while major audits will take place annually.

3. Audit structure/methodology

There will be responsibilities for inspection, audit and review. Questions will be asked and schedules formed as follows.

3.1 Site inspections

These will be carried out monthly both on a rotating basis and randomly as required.

The schedule will isolate:

- the location;
- audit date;
- procedure.

3.2 Audits

3.2.1 Quarterly. Where audits are conducted quarterly, the review will ask the following questions and investigate:

(i) The organization structure – has it changed so as to require changes in the EMS?

(ii) The administrative and operational procedures – have they changed so as to require changes in the EMS?

(iii) Changes in work areas, operations and processes.

(iv) The operation of the EMP review committee in evaluating the documentation and reporting system.

(v) The operation of the EMP review committee in evaluating the performance.

3.2.2 Protocol. The environment manager will use whatever protocol he or she finds convenient for the quarterly audits but will follow the guidelines of ISO 14000.

3.2.3 Annual. Working with the environment manager an outside consultant will carry these out to the requirements of ISO 10000/BS 7750/ISO 14000, and report accordingly in written format.

This report will review the following:

(i) The issues in the quarterly audit above, and those below.

(ii) The conformity of activities with declared requirements.

(iii) The effectiveness of the systems employed.
(iv) Details of any corrective actions recommended in previous audits and their effectiveness.
(v) Conclusions and recommendations.

4. Audit procedure/documents/report

4.1 Executing the audit

The audit procedure will be:

- initial meeting;
- data gathering;
- documentation and compilation (audit findings);
- audit report (closing meeting).

4.1.1 Initial meeting

At each opening meeting introduce the members of the audit team to the appropriate staff and management; spell out the scope, objectives and audit plan; give a summary of the methods and procedures to be used to conduct the audit – for example, site inspection, questions, interviews; agree the communication links between the audit team and the staff; make sure that the audit can proceed properly; and agree the schedule.

4.1.2 Data gathering

The master documents to be used are the control sheets in the Control and Monitoring Manual, in particular the limits set for each issue, in the case of the environmental issues.

In the case of the health and safety issues, both the health and safety records in the manual, and snapshot site inspection of activities (are staff wearing the correct personal protective equipment?) will be employed. Interviews will also be used. Any indications of non-conformity with the environmental management systems criteria will be noted. In addition to examining the results of monitoring activities, the basis of any sampling system will be examined.

4.1.3 Audit findings

All audit findings should be documented. The audit team should review all of their findings to determine which do not conform to the environmental management systems audit criteria. The audit team should then ensure that these are documented in a clear, concise manner and supported by evidence. Findings should be reviewed by the lead auditor with the responsible auditee manager with a view to obtaining acknowledgment of all findings of non-conformity. (There is a Note 9 in the standard: 'Details of findings of conformity may also be documented, but with due care to avoid any implication of absolute assurance.')

4.1.4 Closing meeting with the auditee

After completion of the evidence collection phase and prior to preparing an audit report, the auditors should hold a meeting with the auditee's management and those responsible for the functions audited, to present the audit findings, so that all understand them and agree them. In this way it is hoped that any disagreements can be resolved before the lead auditor issues the report. The final decision on the contents rests with the lead auditor, even where there is still disagreement.

The lead auditor can also make recommendations for improvements to the environmental management system, if this was part of the scope, and these will not be binding on the auditee, who will determine the extent of measures and the means of achieving them to improve the environmental management system.

4.1.5 The working documents for the audit are:

- the checklists and supporting methodologies;
- audit work sheets (with evidence for conclusions to be reached);
- records of meetings;
- forms for reporting audit findings.

All working documents are filed until the audit report has been accepted by management and the client. Full confidentiality requirements will be met.

4.1.6 The audit report (see next section).

5. The audit report

The audit report isolates nine subjects.

5.1 Background

- the identification of the unit audited;
- the auditee's representatives;
- the audit team members;
- the audit date (signed by the lead auditor).

5.2 Objectives

- the agreed objectives.

5.3 Scope and organization

- the audit plan;
- scope of the audit.

5.4. Base of reference

- documents, the targets and controls, stated limits;
- the agreed criteria against which the audit was conducted;
- a summary of the audit process.

5.5 Degree of conformity/non-conformity

– summary of the audit process including any obstacles encountered;
– how the audit and its results met the planned audit criteria;
– whether the system meets the requirements of the stated environmental policy and objectives;
– whether the previous audits and the management review process ensure that the environmental management system continues to properly serve the company.

5.6. The actions required

– inc. the audit findings;
– while the audit report may suggest actions required, the management is responsible for the corrective action needed to correct a nonconformity or to correct the cause of a nonconformity. The auditor may identify a non conformance but will not always be in a position to suggest remedies, and this is not his or her responsibility.

5.7. Opportunities for improvement

5.8. The distribution of the report

Released to management by lead auditor. Distribution to be determined by management.

5.9. Statement of confidentiality

ISO 14000 refinements on ISO 9000 and BS 7750

The early drafts of ISO 14000 have cast further light on the direction in which environmental auditing is evolving. Here are some comments about apparent refinements on previous auditing material.

- The objectives of the audit are to assess the EMS against ISO 14001.
- A lead auditor should be in charge in accordance with ISO 14012 – that is, he/she should have the required experience/qualifications, including a minimum of four years work in the area (probably means at environmental work or auditing).
- A lead auditor should have acted as an auditor throughout at least three com-

plete audits, extending over 15 days (presume that this can also be more audits of less than 3 days making up 15, and can include desk audits of documentation).
- The client determines the need for the audit and initiates it, selects the lead auditor, and determines the scope of the audit.

ISO 14000 has more detail than BS 7750 on format and procedure of audit and report.

13

The health and safety regulations

During the meetings of the technical sub-committees reporting to TC 207 on the module development of the environmental management standard, ISO 14000, the subject of health and safety came up several times. A decision was made to ask ISO to delegate the study of this issue to a committee other than TC 207. This decision maintained the position of health and safety remaining outside the remit of ISO 14000, at least in its early development, a position already established with the national environmental standards such as BS 7750.

This attitude towards such a fundamental issue is inexplicable. The standards do not exclude staff health and safety. They explicitly recognize that health and safety may as an optional issue be managed under the standard. There is now talk of a separate BSI standard for health and safety, a BS 8750, which could become the model for an ISO standard, but all in all the attitude of the committees designing the environmental management standards has been lukewarm towards this issue. One cannot at times but wonder if the architects of the standards fully understand the realities of operational environments where acknowledgment that operational and public safety are environmental issues should automatically include staff health and safety in those issues.

In most countries with developed economies the staff health and safety issues are mandatory under law and carry risks for management of both corporate and individual liability should they be neglected. In Europe they tend to come under government departments separate to those handling environmental matters, such as health and safety authorities under departments of labour. Environmental standards can come under the control of departments of industry depending on how national certification schemes work. What may be keeping the health and safety system separate is that it may be inspected by health and safety authority officers, rather than officers carrying out environmental management standard certification inspections.

Another possible reason for its exclusion is that the EU EMAS Regulation ignored it also. CEN, the European standards agency, is expected to adopt ISO 14000 as the European standard (EN) for environmental management systems, at which point all the national standards bodies with environmental standards, such as the UK, France, and Ireland will drop their versions and adopt ISO 14000, which will also be EN ISO 14000 as the official European standard.

This has left industry with no advice on the matter of health and safety. The environmental management standard expects a system which manages incidents, emergencies, public and process safety. The health and safety authority wants to see a formal management system for staff health and safety, and it has more power in this matter than have the agencies interested in the 'voluntary' environmental standard, where almost every issue will also have legal implications. Companies are all implementing the health and safety regulations, and those implementing systems to BS 7750 or ISO 14000 are finding it sensible to implement all the issues under the environmental management standard. This is fine as far as the environmental certifying inspector is concerned as he or she will simply ignore the health and safety issues, but what about the inspector from the health and safety authority?

In the approach outlined later in this chapter, everything required under health and safety legislation, using Europe as a model, will be satisfied by an ISO 14000 system. The health and safety legislation demands a 'Safety Statement', and while most companies meet this requirement with a vague policy statement hardly worth the paper it is written on, the author's approach in this book is to implement a real system with controls and to write it up in a separate health and safety manual complete with SOPs. The only small fear which the author may have is that health and safety authority inspectors not yet familiar with the sophisticated environmental management system might have difficulty recognizing the safety statement in that form. In such a case the company can cross-reference the policy page of the health and safety manual to a formal safety statement in the appendices which will merely give lip service to what the inspector wants to see. The real system of management will be in the manual and its related controls.

Unlike the environmental, process and raw materials related legislation, the staff health and safety regulations are easy to establish, but require care when built into an updating mechanism as they are constantly being added to, particularly in Europe. This is one of the most standardized areas of European regulations, the reason being that the European Commission has written explicit directives on each of the specific worker health and safety issues and, as each such directive is published, the member states adopt them with little or no change, and make them law through the issuance of national statutory instruments.

The only difference outside Europe is that this process goes on only at the national level; in Europe companies have the advantage of seeing the EU directives in advance, which gives them early warning of coming national legislation. Many opt to implement the EU legislation as it is published, both as a safe best code of practice and a mechanism for ensuring that they are up to date on the law.

The system proposed below is very straightforward, but the reader needs to be warned that although it may be easier for lawyers to know what your health and safety legislation is compared with environmental, these also are issue or task based, and only a manager who can relate the regulations to the actual tasks can come up with meaningful controls. What in effect you are trying to achieve is to protect yourself and your company from any possible claim for damages and, in particular, a charge of negligence which could result in criminal charges in Europe and some other territories.

The recommended approach

Obtain the list of regulations. In general there are around 20 which matter and these are of two kinds:

1. Those which are self-contained, carrying all the details either directly within the regulation (which may also be called a statutory instrument) or in annexes to it.
2. Those which are general in nature (typical being safe workplace and safe work equipment) and require the support of detailed codes of practice expressed in SOPs.

You must scrutinize each health and safety regulation, relate it to your tasks, write an easy to read procedure, design a control mechanism, and, using the written procedure, train your staff.

The practical way to ensure that this is done is to incorporate the health and safety regulations under the environmental management system, so that each of them is controlled automatically. For example, in the approach recommended in this book the fact that each new staff member has been trained is managed in the relevant document in the Control and Monitoring Manual. The production of procedures and training ensures that employees share the responsibility for their well-being, or that it is partially transferred to them from you as manager. Where good procedures and a training scheme exist, managed under a controlled system, it is difficult to imagine a situation where a company or an individual manager can be prosecuted for negligence. The negligence can arise only if a regulation and its necessary controls are ignored. Negligence could come to light either through an inspection from a national health and safety executive inspector, or as a result of a court action brought by an injured staff member whose lawyer has noticed the shortcoming.

What is being recommended here for the health and safety issues is no different from that for the general environmental, process and materials issues. The basis of the environmental management system is the process of scrutinizing the regulations, or codes of practice, and constructing procedures, controls and training material from them.

In Chapter 8, it was recommended that the second half of the Register of Regulations, or a separate register contain all of the health and safety regulations, the actual national statutory instruments, in plastic see-through envelopes at the back of the register, which is usually a ring binder, or in part two in a second ring binder. Devise a separate staff health and safety training course for staff.

What follows below is a sample outline of a comprehensive Health and Safety Manual, together with a list of typical SOPs, hopefully more than most companies will require. It will be seen that all of the health and safety issues, including those which go beyond staff, process and public, are here also. This approach attempts to redress the weakness in the standards which does not appear to recognize that staff and public safety are really inseparable – for example, a process accident could affect both staff and the local community, a fact that appears to have been fully recognized only by the chemical industry.

For convenience, management summaries only can be included in the Health and Safety Manual, so that individual managers can obtain an overview of what each issue involves. The full procedures for each legislated (or related to legislation) task can be in the SOPs. For example, the important matter of emergency response and accident procedures may have to be laid out in full in a separate manual, of many pages. In the approach taken here, this is included in SOP 1.

The sample opposite is a typical list, by no means complete. This is particularly so regarding the SOPS where the titles only will be shown in the H&S Manual with the full text in each SOP.

HEALTH AND SAFETY MANUAL

Table of Contents

Part 1 Administration

continued overleaf

continued

Part 3 Occupational health

Medical services
Eye and audiometric tests
Resources available/welfare
Training programmes

Part 4 Loss control

Audits and reviews
Emergency response
Accident procedures
Security
The management controls
Standards used

The Standard Operating Procedures (or SOPs)

SOP 1	Emergency and evacuation procedures manual
2	Permits to work
3	Safe workplace
4	Noise
5	Safe equipment
6	Personal protective equipment
7	Manual handling
8	VDUs
9	Fork lift trucks
10	Handling of dangerous substances
11	Working in confined spaces
12	Hot work
13	Safety signs
14	Pregnant workers
15	Batteries
16	Compressed air
17	Steam boilers/pressure vessels
18	Contractors/visitors
19	Office
20	Electricity
21	Electrical power tools
22	Compressed air power tools

continued opposite

continued

23	Automatic doors
24	Workshops
25	Window cleaning
26	Work at heights/fragile roofs
27	Ladders
28	Step ladders/trestles/staging
29	Loading bay/truck movements
30	Trucks
31	Exposure to carcinogens
32	LPG
33	Welding
34	Internal vehicles
35	Scaffolding
36	Mobile towers

Any reader needing samples of a full manual should contact Gower about the generic documentation packs.

The European Union health and safety regulations

In the itemized list above only headings have been shown for both the Health and Safety Manual and SOPs as the full contents can run to several pages. As they are so important, typical legislation is shown based on EU regulations. These latter are made into local law by each member state and cover the following areas:

- General health and safety (under the Framework and Safety, Health and Welfare at Work regulation).
- Workplace.
- Work equipment.
- Visual display units.
- Manual handling.
- Personal protective equipment.
- Pregnant workers.
- Temporary workers.
- Safety signs.

- Limit values.
- Asbestos worker protection.
- Carcinogens.
- Biological agents.
- Exposure to noise.
- First aid.
- Electricity.
- Notification of accidents and dangerous occurrences.

Also on the way in the EU are directives for working hours (under dispute in some EU countries at time of writing), young people at work, mines and quarries, offshore, vessels, transport of dangerous goods, exposure to dangerous substances, activities in the transport sector, fair grounds and play grounds.

14

The Responsible Care Programme (RCP)

The origins of the RCP are to be found both in the US and Canada. The Canadians took an existing US programme called CAER (Community Awareness and Emergency Response) and used it as one of the main codes of practice in the seven codes of the RCP. The Canadians, through the Standards Council of Canada, also have the honour of holding the secretariat of TC 207, the overall managing committee for the development of the ISO 14000 series. In 1980 the Canadian Chemical Producers Association (CCPA) created a 'Responsible Care' system by drawing up a number of codes of practice for their industry, including CAER.

In the US, the Chemical Manufacturers Association (CMA) was already under siege, from both a critical public and the draconian powers of the 'Superfund' legislation, the full name of which was 'The Comprehensive Environmental Response, Compensation and Liability Act (CERCLA) of 1980.' The Association was in the middle of the renegotiation process for the re-authorization of the Superfund legislation, due in 1984, when disaster struck in India at the Union Carbide plant in Bhopal, killing 3,000 local people, but not one employee. The real significance of CAER was made clear, for, instead of there being a community awareness and emergency response partnership with the local community, the citizens of Bhopal had rushed to the fence to watch when the emergency took place, running to their deaths instead of an orderly evacuation. There was no system connecting the plant with the community. It marked the end of one debate in the US – about how to recover or create a good public relations image.

The CMA made some momentous policy decisions, including that the whole of the industry, not just Union Carbide, was responsible for dealing with the Bhopal crisis. By the time a second Union Carbide plant at Institute, West Virginia, experienced a toxic release in August 1985, fortunately killing nobody, it had already transpired that many individual plants had contingency plans which did not relate to or inform the local population. The first module of the RCP, CAER, now became CMA policy.

The foundations of CAER are both openness to, and involvement with, local communities. For the first time the industry began to perceive that where they had no chance of ever achieving acceptance with activists, who in turn were the darlings of the media, they could achieve a good image where it really mattered with their neighbours in local communities. But this image had to be based on real, independently verified, facts.

The RCP is a voluntary system, policed by the industry itself, and therefore it allows continuing attacks on the integrity of individual plants. What the industry has found hard to accept and promote is that both standards such as BS 7750/ISO 14000 and regulations such as EMAS are third-party verifications that the codes of the RCP have been fully implemented. This may not be the industry's fault as a general understanding of the relationships between management standards, codes of practice and certification is only now emerging.

The CMA adopted the RCP in September 1988. It has been spreading slowly to other parts of the world since and is well advanced in Europe where its progress appears to be a function of the efficiency of local chemical industry associations, which are members of the European overall body CEFIC. The RCP requires that the chief executive officer of each member company be responsible for the introduction of the programme.

By 1989, the other management codes of the RCP were emerging. The first was CAER followed by pollution reduction, process safety, distribution, waste management, employee health and safety, and product stewardship. From the early chapters of this book the reader will be aware of the author's belief that the RCP can be the overall code of practice for any large or complex industry, and in particular all process facilities, such as food companies, and not just for the chemical industry. The way to do this is to adopt the general guiding principles listed below and just ignore the details of any that might not be relevant. Most companies will find that where an RCP code has no direct-site relevance for them it will have relevance for a supplier issue.

The guiding principles of the RCP are listed below with each followed by the author's comment on its relevance to all industry.

- To recognize and respond to community concerns about chemicals and our operations. [Relevant to all industry]
- To develop and produce chemicals that can be manufactured, transported, used and disposed of safely. [Relevant to all industry if product and service are substituted for 'chemicals'.]
- To make health, safety and environmental considerations a priority in our planning for all existing and new products and processes. [Relevant to all industry.]
- To report promptly to officials, employees, customers and the public, information on chemical related health or environmental hazards and to recommend protective measures. [Relevant to all industry if product and service are substituted for 'chemicals'.]
- To counsel customers on the safe use, transportation and disposal of chemical products. [Relevant to all industry if product and service are substituted for 'chemicals'.]
- To operate our plants and facilities in a manner that protects the environment and the health and safety of our employees and the public. [Relevant to all industry.]
- To extend knowledge by conducting or supporting research on the health, safety and environmental effect of our products, processes and waste materials. [Relevant to all industry.]
- To work with others to resolve problems created by past handling and disposal of hazardous substances. [Relevant to all industry as far as waste outputs are concerned.]
- To participate with government and others in creating responsible laws, regulations and standards to safeguard the community, workplace and environment. [Relevant to all industry.]
- To promote the principles and practices of responsible care by sharing experiences and offering assistance to others who produce, handle, use, transport or dispose of chemicals. [Relevant to all industries where chemicals are used; any industry can have a similar code for co-operation with others in the same business – for example, print and packaging companies sharing environmental information.]

The management codes

The CMA has published detailed codes of management for each of the seven areas of CAER, pollution reduction, process safety, distribution, waste management, employee health and safety, and product stewardship.

These are available directly from the CMA in the US, from the CIA in the UK, equivalent chemical industry associations in all European countries, and from similar bodies where they exist in other countries.

The first code of practice in the Register of Regulations can be the RCP, and the seven detailed codes can be mentioned in the policy statement of the Environmental Management Manual or given in the detail which follows below. This means that the RCP is the top, or overall, policy: that is, the code of practice which will ensure that all other necessary parts are in place. This places the company in a strong position *vis à vis* certification, as it is using a code for achieving environmental probity higher even than ISO 14000. The RCP is the code, while ISO 14000, ISO 9000 and other regimes such as health and safety are the mechanisms for meeting the requirements of the RCP. In court there could hardly be a better demonstrable code of conduct supported by certification of the management system.

The author has examined each of the RCP codes of practice in detail and could find no parts which were not amenable to being achieved under an ISO 14000 environmental management system, and BS 7750 before ISO 14000 became available. In summary, the seven codes of management practice are the seven strands of an overall environmental, health and safety policy.

Companies in Europe can implement quality, environmental management and health and safety systems under ISO 9000/ISO 14000, plus the health and safety regulations, controlled also under ISO 14000, and, if they employ public disclosure, they will also qualify for the EMAS regulation's logo.

An additional advantage is that the RCP appears to anticipate some, if not all, of the coming Phase Two revisions of ISO 9000. We have already demonstrated how CEFIC and the CIA have adapted ISO 9001 to meet environmental requirements, but this has not been accepted by accreditation agencies such as the NACCB and the author cannot see how one can implement an EMS in practice without the structure of a standard such as BS 7750 or ISO 14000. The excellent CEFIC and CIA documents, however, using ISO 9001, are the best yet for the health and safety issues which the standards writers appear not to want to cover.

Summary of the approach to the RCP

Use the RCP as the overall template for policy and requirements and apply ISO 9000 and ISO 14000 as the mechanisms. Treat staff health and safety/public safety/emergency response, as environmental issues, but also contained in a separate health and safety manual, cross-referenced to SOPs, for legal and inspection reasons. If you are in Europe, add public disclosure to ISO 14000 to meet EMAS requirements. To do this publish your results once a year in a ring binder together with policy. Offer it to the media and the community.

The following sample is a proposed format for public disclosure under EMAS.

Policy manual/environmental performance report

Contents

1. *Foreword*
   CEO statement.
   Description of company.
   A company environmental policy statement.
   Highlights of year's environmental performance.
   Community relations programme.

2. *The products*
   Details of products, in particular end products and their contribution to industry or society in general. The meaning of product stewardship in the RCP context of product life cycle analysis. [See Chapter 11 for more information on product life cycle analysis.] Contribution of suppliers of raw materials and components to environmental probity.

3. *The production process*
   Whatever is state of the art, particularly in relation to emissions, discharges, waste, noise, safety and odour.
   Use of resources - energy, water, other materials.
   Technology employed.

4. *The environmental management programme*
   - Objectives and targets.
   - Plans for continuous improvement.
   - Local community measures - *viz*, using local recycling mechanisms.
   - School or other programmes.

5. *The environmental management system*
   - The limits set.
   - Controls.

continued overleaf

continued

- Standards used - viz, the ISO 14000/BS 7750, ISO 9000, RCP, EMAS.

6. *The results*
   - Emissions.
   - Discharges.
   - Noise.
   - Odour.
   - Public safety.
   - Product safety.
   - Staff health and safety.
   - Raw materials.
   - Energy used.
   - Materials minimization (internal to plant including water).
   - Undesirable substances substituted.
   - Number of incidents/complaints/licence infringements.

7. *Communications*
   - How the plant relates to the community.
   - Policy on press enquiries.
   - Where information is available.
   - Contact names and numbers.

For subsidiary site reports CEFIC recommends the following structure:

1. Foreword.
2. Site description.
3. The EMS.
3. The data.
4. Communications.
5. General comments.
6. Contact names.

15

Staff training

Both the ISO 14000 and ISO 9000 standards require that staff be trained. There is a number of levels of training and the author has found it convenient to develop a comprehensive training course utilizing overhead transparency modules which can be used in the following ways:

1. For initial top-management presentation for the main purpose of getting commitment and the decision to go ahead with one or both standards.
2. For the original detailed presentation to the quality/environment manager or project team.
3. For the staff training.

It has also been found useful to use videos, particularly those on the subject of the environment as they add a touch of glamour and break the monotony of the one person presentation. This book will, unfortunately, not allow the reproduction of a full training course but Gower has available both packaged training courses as part of their *Keypac* and *Chempac* products and Gower also has excellent videos. There are several levels of training:

1. The general staff training in quality and environmental matters asked for in the standards.
2. Specific task training for job tasks. Much of the material for this comes from equipment and materials suppliers, and this is difficult to obtain in generic form.

3. Health and safety training. This is compulsory under the law and its neglect exposes managers to personal liability.
4. Specific staff training in environmental tasks. (Turning valves, processing waste and so on.) This training should be covered in SOPs.

The following sample is a proposed outline for a comprehensive training course for a general manufacturer.

Outline of course - general manufacturer

Section 1 General and background
- 1.1 The new environment for business.
- 1.2 Explanation of standards.
- 1.3 The concept of a management system standard.
- 1.4 EU, international and national standards and regulations
- 1.5 Description of key terms.
- 1.6 Historical background.

Section 2 Case-study: manufacturing company

Section 3 The ISO 9000 series

Section 4 Auditing and the ISO 10000 series

Section 5 Certification or registration

Section 6 The ISO 9000 services standard

Section 7 Case study: services company

Section 8 BS 7750/ISO 14000, EU EMAS regulation

Section 9 Case study: ISO 14000

Section 10 Health and safety

The above course can run from short modules of two hours to a full day.

The sample opposite is a similar outline for a chemical/process company.

Outline of course - chemical/process company

Section 1 General and background
- 1.1 The new environment for business.
- 1.2 Explanation of standards.
- 1.3 The concept of a management system standard.
- 1.4 EU, international and national standards and regulations.
- 1.5 Description of key terms.
- 1.6 Historical background.
- 1.7 Overview of situation.

Section 2 The Responsible Care Programme

Section 3 The ISO 9000 series and the CEFIC approach

Section 4 Auditing and the ISO 10000 series

Section 5 Certification or registration

Section 6 ISO 14000/BS 7750 and the EU EMAS regulation

Section 7 Case study ISO 14000

Section 8 Health and safety

To end the chapter, the following pages are samples only of the kind of overhead transparency material which is readily available in the full packages; these packages will also be found very useful for presentation to management.

SAMPLE: OHP 1 - Position of standards

BS 5750 World's first QM standard - model for ISO 9000

EN ISO 9000 Adopted by the EU as the European standard

BS 7750 World's first EM standard - model for ISO 14000

ISO 14000 First international standard on environmental management

SAMPLE: OHP 2 - Four major stages

1. Commitment, planning
2. The project to implement the system
3. Certification
4. The on-going system

SAMPLE: OHP 3 - Elements in the environmental management standard

Elements which can be covered

Traditional environmental

Staff health and safety

Product/service safety/integrity

Public safety

SAMPLE: OHP 4 - Contents sheet of Quality Manual

CLAUSE		
		Foreword/mission statement
1	4.1	Management responsibility
2	4.2	Quality system
3	4.3	Contract review
4	4.4	Design control
5	4.5	Document control
6	4.6	Purchasing
7	4.7	Purchaser supplied product
8	4.8	Product identification and traceability
9	4.9	Process control
10	4.10	Inspection and testing
11	4.11	Inspection, measuring and test equipment
12	4.12	Inspection and test status
13	4.13	Control of non-conforming product
14	4.14	Corrective action
15	4.15	Handling, storage, packaging, delivery
16	4.16	Quality records
17	4.17	Internal quality audits
18	4.18	Training
19	4.19	Servicing
20	4.20	Statistical techniques

16

Implementing the standard

In an ideal world companies would probably implement an ISO 9000/ISO 14000 system incorporating health and safety as one system, and in one project. Some companies may indeed do this. Almost 100,000 companies in the developed economies, however, are already certified for the ISO 9000 standard and these companies now face ISO 14000 as an additional project. A close look at the suggested links between the two standards reveals that there are not that many in practice, unless one takes the radical approach of CEFIC and expands the paragraphs of ISO 9001 to cover environmental as well as quality issues.

Another pressing reason for some companies to implement ISO 9000 first is that most buyers of materials and components in the manufacturing sector, and in particular in general engineering, electronics, medical, chemicals and pharmaceuticals, are demanding it from suppliers. This market-driven motivation may have more urgency than the more compliance-driven motivation behind ISO 14000, as a company may not stay in business without ISO 9000 if it is de-listed as a supplier by its customers.

The accreditation agencies are now bringing certain pressures to bear on the certification bodies concerning the relationship between ISO 9000 and ISO 14000. They do not want the latter to be an add-on to the former, probably because they believe that environment will encompass quality. For first-time systems, they want to see a stand alone EMS, which in later years can be combined with the QMS.

The proposed procedure for implementing the standards is now discussed for both standards, but it can be taken as relevant to each standard implemented separately. The first step for the mover of the project is to read material such as this book. Another very helpful step is to get hold of the kind of package of generic documentation published by Gower. Using such model documentation can reduce the documentation development time from years to a few months. Four months is a realistic time frame for customizing generic documentation to your own requirements.

The standards should be purchased from any one of the 100 national standards agencies which are members of ISO. The basic ones needed are ISO 8004, the vocabulary, ISO 9000–1 and ISO 9004–Part 1 which explain the intentions of the series. ISO 9001 if you design your product, ISO 9002 if you manufacture to a supplied design, and ISO 9004 Part 2 if you are a services company. Either 9001 or 9002 will also be needed for certification purposes. On the environmental side you will need ISO 14000, ISO 14001, and the three auditing standards ISO 14010, 14011 and 14012.

This part of the advice could be frowned on by the architects of the standards, but, as is said elsewhere in this book, until a more practical methodology emerges, this is the only practical advice available. Get hold of a generic Quality Manual for ISO 9001 or ISO 9002 and use the paragraphs under Section 4 to ascertain the elements in your system. These will range from vendor approval and vendor supplied component procedures to shop floor housekeeping and final delivery. A good quality manual will also have a document index at the beginning, which will give you an overall list of not only what documents you require, but what control activities these represent.

The same can be done with ISO 14001. Use the Section 4 paragraphs of the Environmental Management Manual (see Appendix 2) to ascertain what procedures you need, and a similar index of documents to establish what the related controls and procedures are.

Once you are familiar with the material, make a proposal, perhaps utilizing overhead transparencies, to top management or the chief executive officer and get a commitment to go for the standard. The commitment can be recorded by the relevant managers signing a copy of the policy statement taken from either the sample quality or environmental management manuals with the name of your company inserted.

The most basic member of the team is the quality manager or the environment manager. These can be positions held by two separate people, with the latter often the environment/safety manager, or in smaller companies the position can be held by a quality/environment manager. In larger companies there is often a separate safety manager. The quality manager alone may be able to implement and manage a quality management system; the environment manager will need to manage an Environmental Management Review Team, which will meet at least monthly.

On the quality side there are two main areas of documentation and they require reorganization and controls.

1. The documentation controlled under the Quality Manual.
2. The internal physical reorganization and housekeeping. This will involve marking off defined areas such as goods inwards, restricted stores area, finished goods, and setting up inspection systems with pass, hold and fail sections or markings. Some kind of signing-off system for stages of assembled components may also be needed.

On the environment side there are also the two main areas of documentation and physical reorganization and controls. But there could also be capital expenditure as new treatment or scrubbing facilities may be required or purchases made for separation equipment for oils, greases or metal wastes.

Implementation

The procedure for implementing the two standards is so similar that a single approach is shown here which is relevant for either or both of them. It can be broken into two stages, which are the initial steps and the implementation programme.

The initial steps

- Becoming acquainted with the standards.
- Appraising the situation.
- The proposal.
- Obtaining the commitment.
- Outline plan of action.

The implementation programme

- Policy and commitment.
- The detailed plans.
- Organization.

- The initial review.
- The implementation phase.

Becoming acquainted with the standards

The usual ways are to read books such as this one and to purchase copies of the standards from your local standards agency, which is charged with the responsibility of making ISO standards available nationally.

Appraising the situation

The standards documents are written in a legal manner and will be quite general, and the reader must relate them to internal activities, particularly before approaching top management. In the case of the quality system, issues are fairly obvious; this is not so with environmental matters and one could miss a major issue, an indirect one for example, so take care to talk with internal colleagues such as engineers and the purchasing manager to get some feel for the potential issues involved.

A look at the kinds of regulations given as examples in the Register of Regulations in this book will also give a feel for the general issues. One should also use the relevant industrial association for one's own industry or activity to be more fully briefed on the legal situation. The need for legal compliance is a powerful motivation for senior management.

Annexe A to the BS 7750 standard has a paragraph, A.1.2, entitled 'Preparatory environmental review'. This paragraph is aimed at organizations with no existing formal environmental management system. It should help establish the status of a company's conformance to regulations and how far a company needs to go to implement the standard.

However, it is not until one has carried out the initial review (which cannot be done without the go-ahead of management), that one can know how much work will be involved. The initial review needs to cover four areas:

1. The legal requirements.
2. An understanding of the organization's operational effect on the environment.
3. A review or audit of existing practices.
4. A review of past history in this respect.

The proposal

It is unlikely that any manager needs to convince senior management of the need for ISO 9000 at this stage when large buyers all over the world are beginning to demand it from suppliers. It is likely, therefore, that in the case of ISO 9000 a position paper with outlines of potential project plans will be more appropriate than a proposal, but a proposal may be needed for ISO 14000/BS 7750.

One has to approach the chief executive of small- to medium-sized companies and a senior vice president in large companies or corporations. This could be an important career move for the instigator, a once in a lifetime opportunity. While management no longer needs convincing about quality, it may have to be reminded that the three good reasons for a company to decide to go for the environmental standard are legislation, growing market demand and marketing advantage. If the first two are absent, or not yet fully apparent, the third can be the catalyst and, as time passes, the first two will become dominant.

The overhead transparencies for management presentation listed below (and which are shown in more detail in Appendix 3 and can be taken from the kind of training course proposed in Chapter 15) have been used successfully by the author of this book in explaining the environmental management standard to both the proposers of the standard within companies and to senior management.

Overhead #1	The status of ISO 14000
Overhead #2	Elements which can be covered
Overhead #3	The general issues
Overhead #4	The specific issues
Overhead #5	Packaging issues
Overhead #6	The project/procedure
Overhead #7	Attractions for company
Overhead #8	Potential direct benefits
Overhead #9	Potential indirect benefits
Overhead #10	Key elements to be addressed
Overhead #11	More key elements
Overhead #12	The main documented steps

Obtaining the commitment

The instigator should consider sending a memo to the chief executive officer outlining the background to the standards, using information such as that in the overheads above. What is needed at this stage is a commitment to at least perform an IER, as the rest is likely to follow.

What is also needed at this stage is a preliminary audit/review. This early review which will be required within the context of obtaining the commitment also can wait until the implementation phase begins, but on the environmental side many companies are carrying out both preliminary audits and scoping studies. Whether these take place or not, the IER will eventually provide the mechanisms for implementing the system. The point here is to gather what knowledge one can to help with a proposal. It can be an actual audit carried out as part of the preparatory review involving questionnaires, interviews, and shop floor and site inspections.

The least one needs at this stage is to know what the major issues are for the company, to be aware of the main regulations, and to be in a position to do a scoping study to establish the size of the project.

After the initial submission by letter, or verbally, a proposal may be demanded. This can be drawn up as follows:

1. Background.
2. What it means for our company.
3. Relationship with ISO 9000.
4. What are our environmental issues?
5. How good or bad do we appear to be?
6. The need for a preparatory review and audit.
7. Recommendations.

Experience has shown that when the strong legal drivers of the environmental management standard are explained to management, so that they know that it provides them with third-party corroboration of their employment of best codes of practice, commitment results. At least one should come away with agreement for a scoping study or preliminary audit, to reveal the extent of the work needed to be done to implement the system. If it is agreed to carry out a preliminary audit, this can easily be turned into a full IER, and once the results of this are known it is unlikely that any company would not proceed with the full system.

The key driver with ISO 9000 will be customer demand in almost all companies, although experience with US companies suggests that they are conformance driven in the legal sense with both standards. Being able to demonstrate that one conforms to a best code of practice is the best defence in court whether in matters of product or environmental liability.

Outline plan of action

An outline plan of action for either standard could read as follows:

1. Explanation.
2. List of initial steps to be taken.
3. Outline of all steps to certification.
4. Approximate times/resources.

It may be practical to avoid discussing costs until some measure of the benefits is known.

On the following page is the contents list of an outline plan for the implementation of a system to meet the requirements of ISO 14000. Readers could use the material from this book to fill in their own sections, noting that each of the items in this contents list would be on separate sheets.

```
SAMPLE: List of contents


1. Background
2. The project plan
3. Outline of known steps from now to certification
4. The IER
5. Environment Management Programme
6. Approximate times
```

17

Certification

By now the reader will know that the author has considerable reservations about how certification schemes are being applied around the world and believes that some of the concerns that TC 176 has about industry specific versions of ISO 9000 should be addressed at industry specific certifiers and not at companies who are trying to implement practical standards. Another danger not being addressed in ISO circles is that both the expertise needed for implementation of the management standards and certification could become the property of closed shops of self-interest groups, so that ISO 9000 achieves the very opposite of what was intended by assisting in the construction of barriers to enterprise.

An important distinction between ISO 9000 and *ISO 9000 certification* is emerging, with a cloud appearing over the latter. The problem is particularly acute outside of Europe, the US, and a few other developed countries, where there are sophisticated standards agencies and where helpful government and trade associations programmes are in place. This is far from the case in most of the developing countries, where ISO 9000 has become a definite barrier to exports to Europe.

Malaysia serves as an example of how a country can ensure that its industry is not excluded from markets by the employment of ISO 9000, but which at the same time sets up schemes which may inhibit Malaysian enterprise. The Malaysian national standards body is the Standards and Industrial Research Institute of Malaysia (SIRIM). It operates a scheme using consultants, known as the Quality System Consultants Registration Scheme.

Like other countries with vital export industries, Malaysia has been actively promoting ISO 9000 to industry, in addition to providing technology and quality programmes. Speaking to *ISO 9000 News*, Chin Miew Lim, the head of SIRIM's accreditation unit, revealed that the phenomenal growth of ISO 9000 is unprecedented in Malaysia, as it far exceeds the corresponding totals for product certification which was launched 20 years ago.

The background to the scheme for consultants was that local companies had to either bring in outsiders or acquire the knowledge themselves, often by attending overseas courses. As mentioned earlier (see Chapter 2), the Malaysian government already had a grant-aided national quality programme under way to help the development of SMEs.

In July 1990 SIRIM launched its Quality Systems Consultants Registration Scheme which granted formal recognition to qualified ISO 9000 consultants. The objectives of the scheme are to grant 'formal registration' to quality system consultants who meet the scheme's requirements. For a country which has done so much to liberalize trade and get away from public ownership and done it so successfully, the formal registration of consultants may seem to some to be a bit drastic. The registration of consultants has a potential for bureaucracy and the stifling of free enterprise. For example, what happens to the consultant new to the business who may have fresh new, innovative ideas? Or to the one, not formally qualified, who might produce export products from local consultancy experience?

The system maintains a register of qualified consultants, while the industrial technical assistance fund allows SMEs to pay them. There is also an ILAC (international laboratory accreditation committee) type scheme in Malaysia based on the ISO/IEC Guide 25, which is the international guide for the operation of calibration and testing activities for laboratories and for their accreditation.

The international requirements for qualifying consultants are:

- A professional qualification.
- Membership of a recognized national association or institute of quality assurance, such as the IQCM (Institute of Quality Control and Management) in Malaysia or the IQA (Institute of Quality Assurance) in the UK.
- Knowledge of ISO 9000.
- Successful completion of a lead assessor course in ISO 9000.
- A minimum of five years' working experience in quality assurance.
- The completion of five quality consultancy projects.

Ireland introduced a similar scheme for helping SMEs, which had a direct affect of discouraging consultants, who did not want to be subjected to bureaucratic inspections, from working with SMEs. Some of these consultants had ideas for documentation packages and software which they were anxious to try out on

SMEs, but as the SMEs wanted to use state-funded consultants, these enterprising consultants turned to large industry instead. A direct result in one case was that instead of developing a product aimed at small industry worldwide one potential exporter developed a similar package for the chemical industry. What had happened here was that an enterprising product developer had his plans interfered with by a state development agency because of a poorly thought out grants for consultants scheme, of a kind which invited abuse.

A summary of what could happen in the Malaysian scheme, or in a similar scheme in any other small country where ISO 9000 implementation is being assisted by state grants to consultants, could be described as follows. A potential customer, the SME, goes into a high street store (meets with the consultant) and discusses buying help for his or her ISO 9000 system. Before the discussion is finalized, an official from the state granting agency interrupts the operation, perhaps through an advertising campaign, saying, 'Don't buy in that store; go down the road and buy in a store where we will pay half the cost.' One official responding to criticism replies, 'We have to protect the state's investment.' That same official finds it impossible to understand that the grant-aided consultant is adding the grant to what would have been charged anyway, and that the non-qualifying consultant might have a lot to offer both to the SME in question and in further product development to the state as a whole.

We have already seen that certification may be the shadow to ISO 9000. For every benefit offered by ISO 9000, certification may offer a threat. Certification is open to abuse by over-zealous inspectors, it confers police-type powers to petty officials, and it can become a barrier to enterprise to small companies and single traders.

It is not surprising that ISO and its partner organization, the IEC (International Electrotechnical Commission), are now taking an interest in the accreditation of certification bodies. Whether this is wise for ISO remains to be seen, as it may damage ISO's position as the custodian of management standards. The task force set up to look at certification is developing a proposal for a voluntary system to promote the recognition of certification across national borders. Accreditation has followed on after certification as a harmonization process, and accreditation is, as we know, the accreditation of the certifying bodies. Such a system, whatever it is called, will not be voluntary if staying in business is what counts.

Mutual recognition of certification has become an urgent issue for ISO, and for laboratories, test or certification agencies who must operate in the open market. Such bodies must harmonize (for example, to obtain mutual recognition) the following on lines laid down by ISO:

- Requirements of test and inspection methods employed.
- The elements to be tested, inspected or assessed.

- The test, inspection, or assessment report format.
- The evaluation and decision (yes, no) procedure.
- The response to the tested party – certificate, mark of approval.
- Application procedures.
- Accreditation procedures.
- Methods of evaluation of personnel.
- Methods of evaluation of measurement facilities and calibration of test equipment.
- Methods of control of environmental test conditions.

The accreditation bodies accredit the certifiers, while the certifiers may accept the test reports from laboratories, in addition to their own audits and inspections. The guidelines used are ISO/IEC Guide 42 and Guide 2 and the coming ISO/IEC guidelines on the subject of mutual recognition.

Companies in those countries not well served by either, or both, certification and accreditation agencies for ISO 9000 now and shortly for ISO 14000, will face severe problems in getting their products into the developed economies. There may be a certifier, for example in Country X, called 'The National Certification Agency' but unless that agency is in turn accredited by an acceptable and available accreditation body, the bit of paper it issues demonstrating conformance to management standards such as ISO 9000 and ISO 14000 will not be acceptable to sophisticated overseas buyers. Countries which do not have Malaysia's considerable government and economic drive to help local companies will face huge problems.

Those companies in Europe, the US, Canada, Australia, and in all of the advanced Pacific Rim countries will have access to helpful certification agencies; more than 12, for example, in the US and the UK. Companies in other territories may be finding local certification difficult to access, or could be faced with less than efficient local agencies. They should take urgent steps through their local industry and trade associations to get access to industry specific advice and assistance. There could even be industry specific certification schemes, for construction for example, available to them. Unfortunately for them, the expense of sending staff overseas or of obtaining overseas consultants may be added to their existing problems of remoteness.

Here are some steps helpful in obtaining certification to either ISO 9000 or ISO 14000 (still for now in one or more of its embryonic national standards such as BS 7750).

1. Implement the system using generic documentation if possible.
2. Look for and join a support group.
3. See if help is available from your industry association.

4. Use the material in this book, in particular the Quality Manual (see Appendix 1) and the Environmental Management Manual (see Appendix 2) and related documentation, as a general pre-certification checklist.
5. When you do select a certification agency, check with your national ISO body, which will also be your national standards development agency (and there are such bodies in 100 countries), that the certifier is appropriately accredited. ISO has a directory of accredited ISO 9000 certifiers by country. You should find this in the library of your standards body. Such lists do not yet exist for the environmental management standards but existing accredited ISO 9000 certifiers are a safe bet.
6. Select a certification agency which will help you, not try to prosecute you. Ask around.
7. Select one which will first do a desk audit in its own office, with you sending copies of all documentation by mail, thus avoiding being failed on the documentation after you have paid for the expensive site inspection and documentation audit. Any decent agency which has passed your documentation with some changes asked for should be flexible about changes asked for during site inspections. Some changes can be put in hand while the inspector is still with you.
8. Last, but far from least. Someone in your industry has to be first, and that will hopefully be a big company with resources. Go to any length to find a friendly company in your sector which has already successfully gone through the certification process, and ask both for their advice and permission to inspect their site and procedures.

A solution to the many problems caused by certification has to be found, and the ISO/IEC task force looking at the accreditation of certifiers appears to be the only international device for doing this, for now at least.

ISO's very description of this task force reveals its own ambivalent position on certification. Having repeatedly stated that ISO standards are voluntary, that as a non-governmental organization ISO has no power to enforce implementation of its own standards, that it does not operate systems for verifying conformance with the standards, in particular ISO 9000, it adds the big word *nevertheless* in a 1994 ISO press release, saying:

> Nevertheless, in order to assist companies which have invested in ISO 9000 certification by independent quality system registrars, ISO and its partner organization IEC (International Electrotechnical Commission) are developing a proposal for a voluntary system to promote the recognition of such certificates across national borders.

The main recommendation of the task force set up to look at this matter was that ISO/IEC develop a system which will allow mutual agreement at national and international levels, maintain the identity and traceability of certification body certificates, and allow peer evaluation of the certification procedure.

While ISO 9000 and ISO 14000 are excellent management standards developed by an international organization with the best intentions and the highest integrity, their accompanying certification schemes may be administered by local bureaucratic agencies, the staffs of which have no accountability for their actions. Early indications are that the accreditation bodies giving credibility to these agencies will not be offering arbitration or a second opinion.

The author has been attempting to produce benchmark, or model systems, for ISO 9000 and BS 7750/ISO 14000 by industry. These models are based on industry customized quality and environmental management systems which project both documentation and internal steps needed, along the lines shown in this book.

What is badly needed is for an international business or industrial association, such as Chambers of Commerce, to adopt such benchmarks. If a company which has been refused certification finds upon seeking arbitration that its system did indeed conform to the approved model, and the company had lost business as a result of the action of the certification agency, that company could perhaps seek damages in court for its losses. In this way, certification agencies and their officers would be forced to accept accountability for rash actions. This may sound draconian, but no less so than a small business being de-listed as a supplier because of a harsh certification inspection.

Appendix 1

The Quality Manual

The following points are a useful check for the comprehensiveness of the QMS documents in meeting the requirements of ISO 9000:

1. Ensure that the QMS is as complete as the sample which follows.
2. Ensure that it reflects the *real* situation and is not just a paper situation.
3. Ensure that all of the other necessary support documentation is in place, using the broad list which follows in the document index. This list is fairly broad and basic, and one's own company situation may need these documents expanded or added to, but a cursory glance may reveal what is missing. If there are documents here which are not in your company there should be a good reason.

The other documentation

Apart from these quality system documents, you need the following:

1. Task procedures related to shop floor and connected activities – that is, exact instructions for your product and activities.
2. Health and safety procedures. (See the list of SOPs with the Health and Safety Manual.)

And finally

We now have the names of all the documents and the quality manual. What else do we need to do? We need to set out or reorganize the factory to reflect the demands of the standard as expressed in the QMS. This will include:

- Segregation of Goods Inward.
- A separate fenced-off or marked-off Goods Inward Inspection area.
- Segregated areas and labelling/marking systems for pass/fail/hold. These can be green, amber and red marks.
- Stores off limits except to personnel named at the stores access point.
- Inventory control.
- Production control.
- Quality check points identified and an initialling or signing system for those operators passing component between such points.
- Inspection and test routines.
- A finished goods area.
- A calibration and testing system for monitoring equipment.

Adapting the Quality Manual

In many places the Quality Manual sample which follows can be used as it stands with the given text copied. In those places where exact company information should be supplied, the text gives prompts in square brackets ([ ]) or provides an explanatory note (*Note:*).

In other cases, readers should simply discard information not applicable.

Where 'COMPANY' is used throughout, simply replace with your own company name or title.

Issued by:	COMPANY **Quality Manual**	Rev No.: Date:
Signed by:		Page No: 1 of 62

COMPANY INC.

Quality Manual

Cover Page

Page 1 of 62 Date: __/__/__ _

Rev: 001
Quality Manager:
Document Number QM-01

This manual describes COMPANY's quality system and is a mandatory requirement of that system.

Alterations are not permitted without prior approval from the Quality Manager and must be applied using the system for amendment control contained within this document.

0.1 Circulation list

This manual must be strictly controlled and maintained as a confidential document. It may be circulated only to those shown below:

Copy number	*Holder*	*Title*
1	Joe Jonson	Chief Executive
2	Susan Smith	Production Quality Manager
3	Clare Gardiner	Financial Controller
4	Lucy Carey	Production Foreman
5	Joe Lawless	Shop#1 Supervisor
6	Noreen Campbell	Stores Manager
7	Dave Peters	Shop#2 Supervisor

0.2 **Amendment list**

DATE	PAGE NO.	PARAGRAPH NO.	COMMENTS	APPROVAL:	
				NAME	SIGNATURE

0.3 Table of Contents

0.4 Scope and field of application

This Quality Manual relates to COMPANY's manufacturing facility at [here the name of the exact site/facility will appear]. The system covers all elements of the manufacturing facility and all operations on the site from the quality management point of view.

Operations at other company owned sites are not included.

0.5 Document index

Document Number	*Title*
DC-01	Document master list
DC-02	Amendment list
DC-03	Circulation list
DC-04	Organization chart
QM-01	Quality manual
QP-01	Quality plans (overview of inspection, test, audit and review procedures)
MT-01	Measurement and testing routines
IT-01	Inspection and test records
CS-01	Customer specifications
CP-01	Customer performance
SP-01	Supplier/vendor specifications
SP-02	Supplier/purchasing procedures
SP-03	Approved vendor list
SO-01	Sales order processing procedure
CCR-01	Records of contract reviews
DP-01	Design procedures
PDP-01	Product design and development plan
PC-01	Product catalogues
PS-01	Product specification
QF-01	Quote file
SP-01	Safety procedures
SOP-01	Operating procedures
SOP-02	Continued
-03	Continued
-09	Continued

Document Number	*Title*
SOP-00	Special process procedures
IN-01	Inspection procedures, including Goods Inwards, Goods Inward Inspection (GII) and In-process Inspection and Testing Procedure. [These can be in the operating procedures.]
ST-01	Stores procedures
QP-01	Non-conforming procedures
QP-02	Corrective action procedure
QP-03	Non-conforming product review and disposition procedure
CT-01	Calibration and testing of equipment
QP-22	Quality records
QP-23	Training procedure
QP-01	Internal audits
QP-36	Management review
HD-01	Handling and delivery
SC-01	Statistical control procedures
SR-01	Servicing procedures (if any)

[Sundry other documents are shown in Chapter 4.]

0.6 Amendment procedures

The latest revision numbers of the manual are on the wall of the Quality Manager's office as well as in DC-02, the amendment list. The only valid copy of this manual is that shown with the latest revision numbers.

All copies of the manuals and all revisions and additions are controlled by the Quality Manager.

Changes and additions can be suggested by all staff members and co-ordinated through appropriate managers. All final changes must be carried out with the authority of the Quality Manager.

All changes and amendments are recorded on DC-02, the amendment list. This list and all amended pages are then circulated to the holders of each Quality Manual. Holders must insert new pages and destroy old. The Quality Manager may inspect manuals at any time.

0.7 Description of company

The Company

COMPANY was established in Liverpool in 1921. Originally a family-owned company, it now has manufacturing facilities in four countries and offices in ten. The company's original product line of electric motors has been augmented with related products and components but remains the main product.

The company headquarters is still at Stonewall Street, Liverpool, and the main UK manufacturing facility is at Great Yardmouth Street in Liverpool. This Quality Manual is part of the Yardmouth facility's quality management programme, which has been constructed in accordance with the ISO 9000 standard for quality management systems, and this system will relate to this site only in the first instance. Later it is planned to implement systems to the standard, site-by-site for the whole company.

1.0 Management responsibility

1.1 Quality policy

The management of COMPANY has adopted a policy of operating the plant under control of a quality management system, installed and operated along the lines laid down in the ISO 9000 series of standards. It is company policy to operate continuously to these standards, as they apply, and to seek annual registration from National Certifiers.

COMPANY management's commitment to, and policy for, quality are reflected in the company's mission statement, and in the objectives for total quality listed below.

COMPANY's Policy for Quality

To develop a quality system based on ISO 9001 standards to continuous process improvement and the avoidance rather than detection of problems.

To supply quality products and services by aiming to exceed the requirements of our customers.

To establish strong relationships with both customers and suppliers which will contribute to improving the quality of what we sell and purchase.

To use statistical techniques to monitor quality and to identify problems.

To design and build a quality system based upon employee involvement, and the maintenance of the quality policy.

To provide all employees with the training and support needed to supply quality products and services to all customers.

To properly communicate our quality mission and objectives to all of our employees.

To give individual responsibilities and accountability for the quality system to employees.

To establish an environment that supports the production and delivery of high quality products and services.

To actively encourage each employee to realize his or her full potential.

To foster the idea of a team approach within the organization, based on increasing the company's competitiveness by way of improved quality and productivity.

COMPANY's policy for quality and mission statement are displayed as symbols of our commitment and as reminders of our objectives. Each new employee is presented with the policy in the quality training programme.

Signed by: [Titles and signatures of top management to be inserted here with date.]

1.2 Organization

The responsibility for the quality control organization, its administration, system and procedures is delegated to the departmental managers as part of their normal responsibilities (see App. 1 below).

App. 1 The responsibility, authority and interrelation of all personnel who manage, carry out and verify work affecting quality

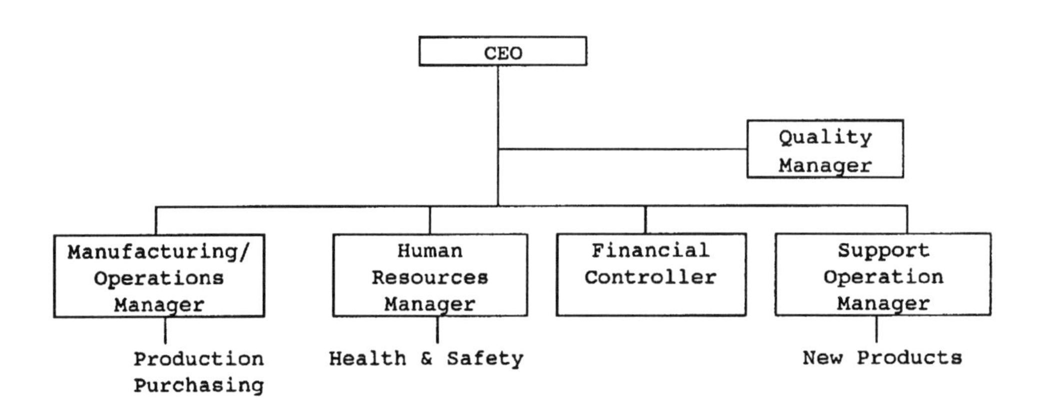

These managers may further delegate their authority to implement quality procedures within specific areas, but will still hold ultimate responsibility. Any such delegation is formally documented.

Certain personnel [The Quality Manager] shall have the organizational freedom and authority to:

- initiate action to prevent the occurrence of non-conformity [which can be system, product or process];
- identify and record any product quality problems;
- initiate, recommend or implement actions as necessary, spelt out and documented;
- ensure through verification the implementation of the actions;
- discontinue the manufacture, delivery and use of non-conforming items until such time as the problem has been rectified.

The SOPs provide the detailed work responsibilities at all relevant levels.

1.2.1 Responsibility and authority
Here list each of your senior managers and specify the responsibilities for each.

Chief Executive
Operations Manager
Plant Manager
Engineering Manager
Purchasing Manager

Financial Controller
Quality Manager
Human Resources Manager
Safety Officer

1.2.2 Resources
The company has committed itself to providing the resources necessary for implementing the quality management system.

Criteria for in-house verification activities, such as inspection, testing and monitoring of all operations affecting the quality of COMPANY's processes and products, and design reviews and audits, are defined in this quality manual, the procedures manual and in work instructions.

Both the Quality Manager and the individual department managers and operating personnel are responsible for the validation of quality. The Quality Manager shall ensure that persons engaged in verification activities have the necessary independence from production to be able to do so.

Design reviews and audits of the quality system, processes and products are carried out by [team as set up by Quality Manager].

Personnel verifying quality are authorized to:
- identify and document any quality problems requiring corrective actions to ensure against the re-occurrence of non-conforming product;

- recommend, initiate and verify solutions to bring about continuous quality and process improvement.

1.2.3 Management representative

The Quality Manager has the authority and responsibility for ensuring that the requirements of this standard are effectively implemented and maintained at COMPANY. Reporting to the Chief Executive, or the Technical Director, he or she has total authority for quality management and the full backing of the Chief Executive, management and board for all actions he/she may deem necessary in carrying out his/her job. This includes the establishment, implementation and maintenance of the system, including any future revisions, such as those proposed in the Phase Two revisions when and as they are made available.

Under no circumstances may his/her decisions about the rejection or re-working or scrapping of production be overridden by production staff or management.

The Quality Manager is responsible for reporting on the performance of the system and for implementing or responding to opportunities for improvement.

The Quality Manager is also responsible for the control of, amendment to, and copies of, all quality manuals.

These responsibilities include liaising with external parties on quality related matters, including certification.

1.3 Management review

COMPANY's quality management system will be reviewed by management personnel having direct responsibility for the system at least once every 12 months.

The review, which is co-ordinated by the quality assurance department, should:

- provide positive and objective evidence that the quality system remains suitable and effective;
- assess the results of internal quality audits;
- identify reports which give an analysis of faults arising during production, customer returns and corrective action results;
- assess potential future requirements that will ensure the system remains suitable and effective.

Each department manager, having carried out a review of the quality system in his or her own area, will present a written report regarding the above issues to the Quality Manager, management representative and Chief Executive Officer.

Corrective actions are then initiated by the Quality Manager, together with the management representative and/or the Chief Executive Officer according to the Corrective Action Procedure QP 02 if appropriate.

Records of the reviews are then filed and maintained by the quality assurance department for a period of at least five years. These records should give details of how the review was conducted, who was involved, the factors considered, the conclusions drawn and the actions taken.

2.0 Quality system procedures

The quality programme at COMPANY shall be documented by policies, procedures or instructions in the form of quality plans and a quality management system, carried out in accordance with written documents. The quality system shall provide control over activities affecting the quality of components and sub-systems to an extent consistent with their contributing to final product quality.

COMPANY recognizes that its employees are the primary factor in the production of quality products. The quality programme shall provide for training of personnel to ensure that suitable proficiency is achieved and maintained.

The status and adequacy of the quality assurance programme shall be reviewed periodically for completeness and adequacy.

The quality system will include:

- quality plans;
- quality manual;
- relevant control documents, procedures and records;
- measurement and testing routines, and equipment;
- agreed levels of acceptability with both customers and suppliers;
- compatibility of documentation and process from design to delivery.

3.0 Contract review

Contract review is detailed in the sales order processing procedure, Doc SO-01, which ensures that all customer requirements are adequately defined and documented, and refers to the customer to ensure the resolution of any disagreements. It also ensures that the company has the capability to meet its contractual requirements.

COMPANY will not accept any order for which it cannot meet the above requirements.

The review ensures that differences between different documents such as tenders, order, contract are resolved.

Records of contract reviews are maintained in document CCR-01.

3.1 Amendment to a contract
A procedure exists for identifying how amendments to contracts are made and carried out within the organization.

3.2 Records
All contract amendments are recorded and the records maintained. These procedures can be both customer designed or designed by our company, depending on the particular customer in question.

4.0 Design control

4.1 General

COMPANY maintains procedures and documentation in order to control its design activities, and to ensure that the resulting design meets all specified requirements.

4.2 Design and development planning

The Design [or Engineering] Manager of COMPANY is responsible for defining each product design and development plan. (See product design and development plan, Doc PDP 01.) A plan is devised for each project concerning new product design or major re-design of existing products, and to assign responsibility for implementation. Plans are updated in the course of the design, development and manufacture of the product.

4.2.1 Activity assignment

The Design [or Engineering] Manager has responsibility for assigning design and development projects to personnel with appropriate resources and training.

4.3 Organizational and technical interfaces

COMPANY's Design [or Engineering] Manager is responsible for identifying organizational and technical interfaces between different groups, as well as documenting, transmitting and periodically reviewing the necessary information for the realization of the product design and development plan.

4.4 Design input

Design input requirements relating to each of COMPANY's products are identified, specified, communicated, and reviewed within the design procedures. (See document DP-01.) In addition, the procedure addresses the settlement of incomplete, ambiguous, or conflicting requirements by those responsible for imposing these requirements.

[*Note:* An important input into design comes from the statutory requirements. There may be a link here with the Register of Regulations in those companies which have implemented environmental management systems, as the register can also contain all product, component and product liability legal requirements. In addition, if the product is subject to the EU CE Mark, this will ensure that all legal requirements of each component are known and met. All of these will reside both in the Register of Regulations, and in the files of the Design [or Engineering] Manager.]

Contracts with other parties such as customers and sub-suppliers or sub-contractors will also contain full specifications for design inputs. This important area will be in the hands of our Design [or Engineering] Manager.

4.5 Design review

The design team will ensure that at any relevant stage of the design, reviews of the progress to date be carried out. These reviews should include as participants representatives of all relevant functions concerned, and other specialist personnel, if required. The reviews will be formally documented and records maintained.

4.6 Design output

The Product Manager is responsible for ensuring that design output is documented and expressed in terms of verifiable requirements. As is required by the standard, design output shall:

a. Meet all design requirements.
b. Conform to referenced specifications/contract/acceptance criteria.
c. In all respects conform to regulatory requirements whether or not these have been stated in the input information.
d. In both hardware/software and any related instructions detail and exhibit in an ergonomically friendly manner those characteristics of the design that are crucial to the safe and proper functioning of the product.
e. Include a review of design output documents before release.

[Note: The ISO 14000 system may also depend on these as product safety issues.]

4.7 Design verification

The Design [or Engineering] Manager is responsible for ensuring that activities for verifying and validating the design are planned, established, documented and assigned to competent personnel according to the design procedures.

Design control measures shall be used to verify that the design output meets the requirements of design input. These measures include:

a. Maintaining and documenting design reviews.
b. Carrying out qualification tests and/or demonstrations.
c. Undertaking alternative calculations.
d. Comparing the new design with benchmarks/similar, already proven, designs, if available.

4.8 Design validation

After successful design verification, validation will be performed on the final product under defined operating procedures.

[*Note:* There is a subtle distinction between verification and validation. This may be related to pre-production testing under real operating conditions.]

Validation follows verification and will be carried out on full finished and (if possible and appropriate) on earlier stages of the product as it evolves.

If the product has different intended uses, a validation process for each may be needed.

[*Note:* Multiple validations may be performed if there are different intended uses.]

4.9 Design changes

The engineering department reviews all requests for design changes or modifications which are identified and transmitted through a report in the Non-Conforming Material Report (NCMR), or Engineering Services Request (ESR) Design changes, found in the non-conformance and design procedures, are initiated and co-ordinated by the [name qualified person], and all changes/modifications are reviewed and approved prior to re-release [by named person]. All design changes are carried out in accordance with the DP-01 procedures.

COMPANY has established procedures for identification, documentation and appropriate review and approval of all changes and modifications. (See design procedures.)

5.0 Document and data control

5.1 General

The document control procedures are as shown in the Quality Manual. (See contents sheets of Quality Manual.) This dictates the policy of the company with respect to document control related matters. COMPANY recognizes the need to maintain an accurate, complete and up-to-date set of drawings, documents and/or specifications relating to ISO 9001, including those of external origin, such as standards and customer drawings.

COMPANY has established and maintains procedures and work instructions to control all documents and data relating to the requirements of this standard and necessary to ensure adequate control. The Quality Manager has also established a document master list, DC-01, which identifies the current revision status of documents and is readily available to halt accidental use.

5.2 Document approval and issue

All documents are reviewed and approved by the Quality Manager prior to issue. (Name here those persons responsible for various documents such as drawings, operating procedures, and so on.) The Quality Manager is responsible for ensuring that the following are in place:

- review and approval of documents by responsible personnel before distribution and use;
- provisions for review/approval signatures and a means of indicating the document revision level;

- numbering and appointment of documents, and copies, to an individual or area of use;
- a register to indicate the document/copy number, and the names and locations of all holders of controlled documents;
- availability of relevant issues of appropriate documents at locations where operations essential to the workings of the quality system are carried out;
- appropriate stamping of documents used for planning or similar purposes that have not received final approval (with DO NOT USE signs stamped or similar;
- document revisions issued to holders of obsolete documents; removal of obsolete documents.

5.3 Document changes/modifications

COMPANY has established and will maintain a document control procedure, to ensure that:

a. The correct issues of relevant documentation are in the correct places where needed by approved personnel.
b. Obsolete copies have been removed.
c. Changes and modifications to documents are reviewed and approved by the same personnel or departments that carried out the original review and approval unless specifically designated otherwise.
d. All documents are controlled under our document control procedures including a master list, and documents subject to change are reissued after a practical number of changes to avoid unnecessary paperwork.

6.0 Purchasing

6.1 General
COMPANY shall ensure that all purchased parts/products meet the specified requirements in accordance with the supplier/purchasing procedures, document SP-02.

This shall be done as:
- all purchased parts go through goods inward inspection (GII) and are inspected according to the GII procedure, shown in document IN-01, inspection procedures. The GII procedure takes into account all requirements and the need where necessary for certificates of conformance.
- upon request, suppliers shall provide COMPANY with reliability test data and standards used on each component by part number.

6.2 Evaluation of sub-contractors
The purchasing department, with the assistance of quality assurance, is responsible for the selection, qualification and disqualification of COMPANY suppliers. This will be accomplished with the aid of an approved vendor list, document SP-03. Vendors will be added to the approved vendor list after five different delivery batches have passed GII [or your own rules]. Approved vendors who fail five continual delivery batches will be removed from the approved vendor list.

The Quality Assurance and purchasing departments are

responsible for ensuring that all non-conforming vendor supplied material is dispositioned in a timely manner.

COMPANY will select vendors based on the records of their quality performance, namely:

a. Their ability to meet specified requirements and/or specifications conformance.
b. The reasonable pricing factors of unit components.
c. Timing of deliveries as requested or specified on the purchase order.

The quality department is responsible for performing vendor audits. The vendor audit procedure, found in document SP-02, supplier/purchasing procedures, dictates the policy of the company with respect to vendor audit related matters.

The type and extent of the control exercised by COMPANY on its suppliers depends on the type of product and how the sub-contractor has performed in the past.

6.3 Purchasing data

The purchasing department is responsible for ensuring that all purchase orders contain a complete description of the material ordered including, by statement or reference, all applicable requirements for manufacturing, inspecting, testing, packaging and any other requirements. In Section 4, under paragraph 4.6.3, the standard states what these can include, which in effect is all the descriptive data which amount to full specifications, with type, class, style, grade or other identifications.

COMPANY refers to this data as the supplier specification, which will have a title.

[*Note:* If appropriate, state exactly what specifications are needed here, remembering that sophisticated suppliers are already likely to be supplying full specifications in their catalogues or sales or contract material.]

Copies of all applicable purchase orders will be provided to Goods Inwards Inspection.

Production shall be responsible for providing the purchasing department with information regarding any unusual or unique requirements such as source inspection, certificate of conformance, inspection system or quality programme requirements.

COMPANY reviews and approves purchasing documents for adequacy of specified requirements prior to release.

6.4. Verification of purchased products

COMPANY may conduct plant surveys at the premises of subcontractors/suppliers with permission and with supplier participation. Verification by COMPANY, however, neither acquits its suppliers of their responsibility to provide acceptable product nor precludes subsequent rejection.

If COMPANY, or a representative of the company, decides to carry out verification at the vendor's plant, this cannot be used as sole evidence of control of quality by the sub-contractor/supplier.

COMPANY, through GII, shall still check purchased product for conformance to specification even after supplier/sub-contractor audits to ensure the continuation of quality parts.

COMPANY's customer may also carry out verification of the sub-contractor's premises and systems. This may not be used as the sole evidence of conformance by the sub-contractor, nor does it change the demand for the company to meet requirements or act as corroboration that these are fully met.

7.0 Control of customer supplied product

Standard procedures for verification, storage and maintenance are in place for all material supplied by a customer for inclusion in the product ordered. Systems are maintained to ensure that material is used only for the customer's product. Where the product is found to be unsuitable, or where product is lost or damaged, this shall be recorded and subsequently reported to the customer.

Regardless of customer verification, the company is responsible for proper product delivery to customer.

8.0 Product identification and traceability

Procedures will be maintained to ensure that material will be identifiable during manufacture, delivery and installation, by way of drawings, specifications or documents. The following procedures are in place:

- the Materials Manager has responsibility for ensuring that incoming materials are identified at incoming inspection. Records are kept to identify these materials by part number and other appropriate purchasing record.
- in-process materials are tagged.

[*Note:* Here outline the system you use for ensuring identification and progress of the part through the operation; viz. a tagging and signing-off procedure which traces who has done what. For example production units, or orders, are accompanied/identified by means of a job/operation sheet, with part number and description, routing, position on the production line, and initialled status. Describe also the methods of identifying components in accordance with their status; incoming, stores, production line, finished product.]

- an initialling system [describe] is used by the operators to ensure traceability.

9.0 Process control

9.1 General

Relevant departmental managers are responsible for identification, planning and servicing of processes directly affecting quality, and ensuring that these processes are carried out under controlled conditions, which include the following requirements:

- documented work instructions specifying the method of production and installation, in particular at those points in the process where inadequate work could affect quality;
- the correct workplace, equipment, processes and production procedures;
- relevant standard operating procedures, data sheets and safety instructions, produced to standards and codes of practice;
- adequate monitoring and control of activities;
- the relevant certification/measurement/calibration/approval of processes and equipment;
- standards, specifications or other criteria for workmanship which are either written or expressed through models/benchmarks/representative samples;
- the proper appropriate maintenance of equipment.

9.2 Special processes

Special processes, defined as having results which cannot be fully verified by inspection and testing of the product, and where deficiencies may become apparent only after the product is in use, are subject to a number of extra rules and safeguards:

- special processes demand continuous monitoring and compliance with documented procedures to make sure that the special requirements are met;
- they should be carried out and monitored by qualified personnel using documented work instructions or guidelines;
- special processes are qualified and comply with all the requirements listed under section 4.9.1 of the standard;
- records are maintained for qualified processes, equipment and personnel, as appropriate.

The following are considered to be the special processes at COMPANY and are subject, therefore, to the requirements of this particular clause:

- Argon forging;
- Lap plating [imaginary examples];

10.0 Inspection and testing

10.1 General

COMPANY has established and maintains documented procedures for inspection and testing activities to verify that the specified requirements for product are met. The required inspecting and testing, as well as the corresponding records are documented in the quality plan. (See document QP-01, quality plans.)

The inspection procedures are in document IN-01 (these can also be in the SOPs). Non-conforming and corrective action procedures are contained in documents QP-01, non-conforming procedures, and QP-02, corrective action procedures.

10.2 Receiving inspection and testing

10.2.1

The Product Manager [or name] is responsible for ensuring that incoming product is not used or processed until it has been inspected or verified as complying with the specified requirements. (The exception to this rule is described in 10.2.3.) Verification is in accordance with document IN-01, inspection procedures.

The following elements are covered in the receiving inspection and testing routine:

- appropriate testing measures (*viz.* are you testing paint thickness?);
- means of handling rejections/non-conforming materials;

- procedure for passing acceptable product;
- documentation of the above.

10.2.2
If certain or much control is carried out at the supplier's premises such as in a ship to stock or to production situation, or a zero defect delivery arrangement, this procedure can be adapted accordingly, or the supplier's procedure substituted here.

10.2.3
Where incoming product is needed and released for urgent production purposes, it is identified and recorded in such a way as to allow its recall and replacement in the event of non-conformance with specified requirements. (Name the special procedure document here.)

10.3 In-process inspection and testing

a. COMPANY's Product Manager (or other) is responsible for ensuring that test product is inspected, tested and identified as required, and not let pass on through the process unless it meets the appropriate tests (specify in document IN-01, inspection procedures).
b. The Product Manager must also establish product conformance to specified requirements through process monitoring and control methods. This is done in accordance with COMPANY's document IN-01, in-process inspection and testing procedures, which addresses such issues as:

- the use of appropriate methods, work standards, and inspection plans for inspection and testing;
- control of nonconforming materials;
- type of test/inspection;
- non-conformance procedure;
- records and reports.

c. Product must be held and not used or further processed until the required inspection and tests have been completed or the product has been otherwise verified as conforming to specified requirements.
d. The Product Manager is responsible for identifying nonconforming product.

10.4 Final inspection and testing

COMPANY's documented procedures require that all specified inspection and tests, including those specified either on receipt of product or in-process, have been carried out and that the results meet the stipulated requirements.

COMPANY carries out final inspection and testing in accordance with the inspections procedures, in document IN-01, to show evidence of product conformance to specified requirements.

The Product Manager is responsible for ensuring that no product is despatched until all activities stipulated in the quality plan are satisfactorily carried out. The corresponding data and documentation must be available and authorized.

10.5 Inspection and test records

COMPANY has created and maintains records showing where products have passed inspection and testing and therefore meet all of their specified requirements. (See document IT-01, inspection and test records.)

Documents cover both pass and non-conformance. Final release authority is identified and recorded.

11.0 Inspection, measuring, and test equipment

Documented procedures, as in document CT-01, calibration and testing of equipment, have been established and are updated to control, calibrate and maintain all inspection, measuring and test equipment used by COMPANY in order to demonstrate the conformance of product to the specified requirements. This refers to all such equipment, whether it is owned by COMPANY, or on loan provided by COMPANY's customers. The equipment is used in a way which ensures that measurement uncertainty is known and is consistent with both the measurement requirements and capacity.

Equipment shall be checked before release to production and at intervals described in document CT-01 and the results documented.

Any equipment which is used to measure any parameter, which if inaccurate would critically affect quality, is included in the calibration system. A calibration procedure is shown in document CT-01, calibration and testing of equipment, which includes a list of equipment requiring calibration and the frequency at which calibration is required. The equipment is calibrated against certified equipment having a known legitimate relationship to nationally recognized standards.

11.1 Control procedure

A calibration schedule chart (also in CT-01, calibration and testing of equipment) is available from the Quality Manager.

Equipment in the calibration system will have a label affixed to it giving details of the next calibration date. Sometimes, this label is affixed by an external accredited calibration house. The date on this label may differ to the COMPANY calibration schedule in which case the COMPANY schedule will take precedence. The COMPANY schedule will ensure that the calibration date is within that recommended by the external accredited calibration house.

All calibrations are traceable to a national standard. There is a process in the documented calibration system, defined for the calibration of inspection, measuring and test equipment, including details of equipment type, unique identification, location, frequency of checks, check method, acceptance criteria and the action to be taken when results are not correct.

When equipment is found to be outside calibration, it is immediately removed and brought to the Quality Manager. If possible, the equipment is replaced and sent for recalibration.

There is a corrective action procedure, within the calibration procedure, with instructions regarding the implications to quality caused by the item concerned. Where equipment is found to be out of calibration, the Quality Manager will also assess and document the validity of previous inspection and test results.

It is the responsibility of the Quality Manager to ensure

that the calibration schedule is maintained. A calibration file exists for each item in the calibration system giving details of past and present calibration results.

The Quality Manager must ensure that the environmental conditions are suitable for calibration, inspections, measurements and tests being carried out. He/she must also ensure that the handling, preservation and storage of the equipment is such that the accuracy and fitness for use is maintained.

All operators utilizing inspection/test equipment are responsible for ensuring that equipment is within calibration by checking calibration labels.

Every item of test and measuring equipment shall have an inventory number assigned to it upon receipt and shall be visibly attached unless size or application makes it impractical.

The Technical Director is responsible for ensuring that any equipment used for measuring purposes is suitable for that application.

Items of measurement and test equipment classified as inactive or used as a reference and not requiring calibration shall be so identified by using a `Calibration Not Required' label.

Quality assurance shall ensure that any sub-contractors or

vendors used for device design and/or manufacture have a calibration system satisfying the minimum requirements of the COMPANY calibration system. This will be done through vendor audits, as described in document SP-02, supplier/purchasing procedures.

Records of both calibration test results and status will be maintained.

In cases where equipment is found 'out of sync' recheck the validity of previous inspections.

12.0 Inspection and test status

COMPANY identifies the inspection and test status of all products by using markings, authorized stamps, tags, labels, routing cards, inspection records, test software, physical location designations, or other suitable means (name ones used - for example, tag attached to emerging product with initials from each operator for each relevant stage passed) which indicate the conformance or non-conformance of the product with regard to the inspection or tests performed. The identification of inspection and test status is maintained throughout the manufacture and installation of the product to ensure that only product that has passed the required inspections and tests is dispatched, used, or installed.

a. The manager of the department carrying out the inspection and testing is responsible for identifying the inspection and test status of the product (or perhaps each operator).
b. Staff members responsible for releasing conforming product are also responsible for 'signing off', either or both tag and inspection and test report.
c. Staff members who identify non-conforming product in the course of inspection and test, are responsible for following control of non-conforming product procedures as detailed in section 13.0 below.

13.0 Control of non-conforming product

13.1 General

COMPANY's Quality Manager is responsible for establishing and maintaining documented procedures (see document QP-01, non-conforming procedures, and document QP-02, corrective action procedures) to ensure that product not conforming to specified requirements is clearly identified and isolated to prevent unintentional use or installation. In addition to procedures, there are clearly marked holding areas for reject, re-work and passed product, which bear the red, orange and green colours for the corresponding conformance tags attached to product.

The controls in these procedures include identification, documentation, evaluation, segregation, disposition of non-conforming product and notification to the departments concerned.

13.2 Non-conformity review and disposition

COMPANY's non-conforming product review and disposition procedure is complied with by all personnel who identify non-conforming material, in accordance with document QP-01, non-conforming procedures.

Responsibility for the review and authorization for the disposition of non-conforming product/items is with the Quality Manager. The Quality Manager will assess all rejects and decide on the required actions.

Non-conforming items are either rejected/scrapped, re-worked in-house to meet requirements, accepted with or without repair by concession, or regraded for alternative use.

Repaired or re-worked product is re-inspected in accordance with the normal documented procedures.

Where it is stipulated by the contract, proposed use or repair of non-conforming products must be reported for concession to the purchaser.

Any items which are rejected or re-worked will be documented and this documentation will be used as feedback to the vendor and the purchasing department.

Exact descriptions of what constitutes repair or re-work as distinct from reject non-conformity must be recorded.

The Quality Manager may at times be unqualified to make decisions on items. When such a situation arises, the Production Manager, Materials Manager, Technical Director or Engineering Manager may become involved.

14.0 Corrective and preventative action

14.1 General

The Quality Manager shall initiate corrective action requests whenever quality records indicate that defects are not isolated occurrences. Corrective action requests shall apply to purchasing, manufacturing, testing or any other part of the manufacturing process that may result in non-conforming product.

14.2 Corrective action and preventive action

Corrective action will extend to the performance of suppliers and vendors and will be responsive to data and products received, or returned, from customers. Procedures have been established, and are documented, in accordance with document QP-02, corrective action procedure, and maintained for the following:

- examining the reason behind the non-conformity of product;
- identifying the corrective action to ensure that the problem does not recur;
- analysing the processes, work operations, concessions, quality records, service reports and customer complaints to identify and rule out possible reasons for the non-conforming product;
- analysing trends in processes or performance of work to prevent non-conforming production;
- analysing data and examination of product scrapped or re-worked to determine extent and causes;
- introducing preventative measures to deal with problems

to a level tantamount to risks encountered;
- introducing the required improvements and corrections;
- initially reviewing the adequacy of corrective measures;
- subsequent monitoring of the effectiveness of the corrective action taken;
- reaction to customer complaints or reports of nonconformance from the market.

Document QP-02, corrective action procedure gives more detail on this subject.

15.0 Handling, storage, packaging, preservation and delivery

15.1 General
Procedures exist in document HD-01, handling and delivery, which detail the required specifications for correct handling, storage, packaging and delivery of all products and product parts connected with COMPANY manufacturing and test.

15.2 Handling
Handling is performed in accordance with the handling procedures in the above document, which stipulate prevention of damage or deterioration. The procedure covers fragile material, maintaining the stores in a hygienic condition in order to highlight any deterioration of parts, keeping all parts/products off the floor and away from direct contact with walls, etc.

Where specialized handling, such as unloading from tankers, or the receipt of dangerous substances is involved, detailed SOPs will be written to cover these.

15.3 Storage
Material is stored within the stores area as defined in the stores procedure, document ST-01. The storage area should be deemed secure enough to prevent damage or deterioration of product, waiting for use or delivery. This area is restricted to authorized personnel only. It is the responsibility of the storeman to adequately document items entering and leaving the stores. The condition of the product in stock is assessed at intervals appropriate to the nature of the product. The

area will be audited at least once a year according to the systems audit procedure in document QP-01, internal audits.

In the case of flammables these will be securely segregated. In the case of bulks fuels and chemicals, these will be in bunded tanks or tank farms.

15.4/5 Packaging and preservation
Packing is performed as detailed in the packing procedure, document HD-01, handling and delivery, to ensure conformance to specified requirements. Further to this, every product or batch of products receives a final audit inspection after packing. This is done on a sample basis, but acts as a constant check on packing to ensure adequate protection to the product, correct address, etc. Packaging controls shall ensure that all product is identified, preserved and segregated from initial receipt until such time as COMPANY's responsibility for the product ceases.

15.6 Dispatch/Delivery
Dispatch is performed as detailed in the dispatch procedure, document HD-01, handling and delivery. Carriers of shipments to customers are constantly assessed. When a shipment is sent, the customer will be contacted two days later to verify receipt of shipment. Dispatch invoices will not be given to Accounts until verification of delivery is received. If a carrier delays the delivery, loses a shipment or is found to be at fault, they will be requested to give an explanation and if this is unreasonable, will not be used again.

16.0 Quality records

Quality assurance is responsible for all quality records. This includes establishing and maintaining procedures for identification, collection, indexing, filing, storage, maintenance and disposition of quality records. The quality records are mainly:

- minutes of manager's meetings and associated documents;
- minutes of management review meetings;
- details of any product which is recalled;
- customer returns;
- customer complaints;
- details of disposal/scrap and non-conforming product(s);
- details of any internal/external quality audits;
- records of statistical analysis or pass/fail quantities and fault descriptions;
- calibration records;
- certificates of conformance;
- product approvals;
- the Quality Manual;
- all the supporting control records.

The quality records of certain sub-contractors are also included in our own records.

These records give further assurance that products are manufactured according to the correct procedures and the quality system operates effectively.

Quality records are stored so as to minimize deterioration and are retained for a minimum of three years.

The Quality Manager is responsible for the general upkeep, filing, storage, identification, indexing and collection of all the quality records. The records are stored both in hard copy and on our computer system.

Where it is contractually agreed, customers will have access to our quality records for an agreed period for the purpose of evaluation.

17.0 Internal quality audits

A systems audit procedure (document QP-01, internal audits) exists which gives details of audit schedules and a check-list to be used to verify the correct operation of each department. A record of all audits will be kept by the Quality Manager. The audits are designed to ensure that procedures in the quality system are correct in themselves and adhered to in practice.

All departments will be audited at least once a year. Certain activities, judged to be more important, will be carried out more frequently. All audits will be unannounced and carried out on a random basis.

Audits will be the responsibility of the Quality Manager, who may call upon the following to carry out the audit, if he/she chooses to do so:

- outside consultant;
- technical department staff;
- production staff;
- engineering staff;
- marketing/PR as required (for marketing and PR functions).

The quality management system in all aspects from procurement to final inspection and test, including customer feedback, will be used as the basis of the audit.

A checklist reflecting the key activities in the system will be drawn up for each audit, along the lines of the next document.

Audit checklist

[*Note:*
One can simply make reference to the audit procedure here (document QP-01, internal audits), but it is so important that some further suggestions are made.

One practical way to construct the audit checklist is to use a pre-certification checklist, in which everything the inspector might look for is included and to select the elements required. For example, one might want to audit everything on the list only before each certification audit, if one knows when that is, or once or twice a year.]

Function to be checked	In order	Deviation
Select from pre-cert- ification list		
[for example]		Minor Moderate
Vendor evaluation		Substantial Serious
Incoming inspection		(plus action recommended)
Quarantine procedures		
Documentation		
Production controls Point A Point B Point C Point D		
Documentation		
Final inspection		
Customer complaint procedure		

Function to be checked	In order	Deviation
Enquiries and orders		
Control of documentation		
Quality manual		

Audit report

Department ____________________

Section ____________________

Supervisor ____________________

Employees ____________________

____

____

____

Findings

No deviations found ____________________

Following deviations found ____________________

____

____

____

Action proposed: ____________________

Auditor's signature ____________________

Manager's signature ____________________

Date __/__/__

Date __/__/__

The results of all audits are documented in [specify] as laid down in document QP-01, internal audits, and are brought to the attention of personnel with responsibility for the areas audited. The Quality Manager is responsible for carrying out immediate corrective action for any deficiencies found.

In all cases where non-conformances were found a follow-up review will be scheduled to ensure that corrective action has taken place. Audit results will form an important input into management reviews.

The whole audit procedure has been designed using as guidelines the ISO 10000 series of standards for quality audits.

18.0 Training

It is the responsibility of the Quality Manager to report on the status of the training of staff as it affects quality, and to maintain records of all staff training status.

There are three sets of training material, which are:

- a general half-day orientation course in quality management for all staff;
- detailed task training in every case where an activity has quality implications - with procedures detailed in SOPs;
- health and safety and environmental training covered under the environmental management system.

General management is responsible for identifying training needs and providing training as it affects quality within each of their functions. They may use the Training Manager or Quality Manager for this as they see fit, but training, like quality, must be embedded within each operational function.

Specific assigned tasks will be carried out by those qualified on the basis of education, training and experience, as relevant.

The training material available is as follows: [Specify the actual videos, courses, books, workshops.]

The training manual is document [specify]. This material

will be reviewed annually by the Quality Manager and reviewed also in audits and in the annual review of the system.

This is a sample of an employee training log.

Name	Status	1	2	3	4	etc.
J Brown	Tech 1	7/1/91	15/5/94	3/9/91		
		Department ———				
		Training office ——				
		Date completed –/–/–				

Task numbers must be cross-referenced to task names: that is, machinery, polishing, and so on.

19.0 Servicing

COMPANY maintains procedures for providing services that meet specified requirements and ensure a high level of customer satisfaction. [Specify documentation/location of procedures.]

Special services for customers include the following activities:

- customer interface service;
- provision of a field service;
- product warranty management;
- provision of service parts and training;
- customer complaints service.

The Sales Manager is responsible for co-ordinating customer service activities at COMPANY, and for maintaining appropriate records to document customer service performance. (See document CP-01, customer performance.)

20.0 Statistical techniques

20.1 General

COMPANY recognizes the value of statistical techniques for assessing, controlling, and improving our quality system and processes. Statistics are used to show current levels of quality, to identify where quality improvement resources and efforts should be directed, and to show the effectiveness of past efforts.

All managers have a responsibility for establishing methods and instructions for the beneficial application of statistical techniques.

20.2 Procedures

The following statistical methods are used at COMPANY to support process control and defect prevention, to measure machine capabilities and levels of quality, and to identify areas for quality improvement.

[Specify.]

Appendix 2

The Environmental Management Manual

Explanatory note

As this book was being written, the only environmental management standard published in final form, and the only one available for certification purposes, was BS 7750, and other national versions, the status of which was not fully certain from the point of view of accredited certification. Because readers will be seeking certification before ISO 14000 may be published in its final form, the Environmental Management Manual in this appendix is therefore modelled upon the requirements of BS 7750, with draft and anticipated requirements of a final ISO 14000 included, cross-referenced to the clauses of the early drafts of ISO 14001. The BS 7750 and ISO 14001 clause numbers are not exactly similar so the sequence used here is BS 7750 not ISO 14001, although the latter are given. The author believes that the early drafts of ISO 14001 have shortcomings and where the architects of the standard have tried to change BSI wording the text suffers. This appendix, therefore, also reflects how the author thinks an environmental management manual should be written, and is not a slavish copy of the text of either standard.

The Manual

If you wanted to do what is apparently frowned upon in certain ISO technical committees, and get hold of the document which would give you a checklist of what you need to do to get certified, the Environmental Management Manual is that document. Such a course of action is not recommended but, just as many people starting out on ISO 9000 did so by acquiring a generic quality manual, many will also do that for ISO 14000 with an Environmental Management Manual.

The simplest way to demonstrate this important document is to provide a generic example, which appears to fly in the face of the critics of this approach, but the author has found no other practical way. Note how the manual is cross-referenced to Section 4 of ISO 14001. Section 4 is fundamental to both ISO 9001 and ISO 14001, as it details the system elements.

What follows now is a sample Environmental Management Manual.

Issued by:	COMPANY **Environmental Management Manual**	Rev No.: Date:
Signed by:		Page No: 1 of 36

COMPANY INC.

Environmental Management Manual

Cover Page

Page 1 of 36 Date: __/__/__ _

Rev: 001
Environment Manager:
Document Number EM-01

This manual describes COMPANY's environmental management system and is a mandatory requirement of that system.

Alterations are not permitted without prior approval from the Environment Manager and must be applied using the system for amendment control contained within this document.

0.1 Document index

Document number	*Title*
EM-1	Environmental Manual
QM-1	Quality Manual
ERR-1	Register of Regulations
ERE-1	Register of Effects
CMM-1	Control and Monitoring Manual
S-1	Safety Statement
EP-1-11	Environmental Procedures
EP-11	Preventative Maintenance System
QP-1	Non-conforming Product
QP-2	Corrective Action
QP-22	Quality Records
QP-23	Training Procedure
QP-24	Customer Returns
QP-30	Internal Audits
QP-36	Management Review
TS-14	Environmental Training Syllabus
QD005	Approvals Sheet
BS 7750	Environmental Management System Standard
Booklet	Training course [use own reference number]

0.2 Table of contents

0.3 Amendment procedure

Reference:	Quality Manual (QM-1, Section 2.1)
Document Control	QP-7
Document Change	QP-8

0.4 Description of company

(Cross-reference to ISO 14001, Section 4, clause 4.0)

COMPANY was established in Liverpool in 1921. Originally a family-owned company it now has manufacturing facilities in four countries and offices in ten. The company's original product line of soap has since been augmented with a range of chemical products. [A brief description of the company's activities and products will suffice.]

The company headquarters is still at Stonewall Street, Liverpool, and the main UK manufacturing facility is at Great Yardmouth Street in Liverpool. This Environmental Management Manual is part of the Yardmouth facility's programme to implement an environmental management system to the requirements of BS 7750, and this system will relate to this site only in the first instance. Later, it is planned to implement systems to the standard, site-by-site for the whole company.

1.0 Environmental management system

COMPANY has prepared and implemented an environmental management system (EMS) which ensures that the effects of the activities of the organization conform to our environmental policy and associated objectives and targets. In implementing this EMS, COMPANY has taken account of any pertinent codes of practice to which it subscribes. The objectives of the EMS are the meeting of the requirements of the company policy on environmental, health and safety, and public safety matters, and all of the related regulations and good codes of practice.

This system is fully documented in accordance with ISO 14001/BS 7750, and is supported by documented procedures at all levels.

The EMS is part of an overall environment management programme, which monitors the progress of the EMS and also sets objectives and targets.

The EMS is linked with our ISO 9000 quality management system and certain sections amenable to being handled under the ISO 9000 system, as per the suggested links in the ISO 14001/BS 7750 standard, are so handled.

1.01 Planning (ISO 14001, clause 4.2)
The first step in our planning process was the carrying out of the Initial Environmental Review (IER), which provided the first inputs to our EMS.

All relevant and particularly significant issues and their effects, both in direct and indirect activities, and from the points of view of pollution and resource usage, were examined in the Environment Management Programme (EMP), and recorded and controlled in the Register of Effects and Control and Monitoring Manual (ISO 14001 clause 4.2.1). This data is kept up to date.

A fundamental part of our planning and implementation process is the maintenance of our Register of Regulations (ISO 14001 clause 4.2.2).

The major plan which ensures that we strive for continual improvement is in our targets and objectives, which are managed as part of the Environment Management Programme (EMP). (ISO 14001 clause 4.2.3)

The Environment Management Programme (EMP) is maintained by the Environment Manager and Environmental Management Review Team, and is detailed in the documented procedure of that name (ISO 14001 clause 4.2.4).

2.0 Environmental policy (ISO 14001 clause 4.1)

Our policy is to fully comply with both the limits set by our EMS and all statutory requirements and to meet our set targets and objectives, in a programme of continuous improvement.

To achieve this, we will implement an environmental management system to the requirements of ISO 14001/BS 7750, using that system in turn to manage all health and safety and public, process and product safety issues.

Our policy can be described as operating to the quality, environmental and health and safety levels expected from a company meeting the requirements of both the law and the best industry codes of practice.

It is also our policy to use our EMS plus public disclosure of policy and environmental performance to apply for and obtain registration to the EU EMAS Regulation [for companies in the EU]. We will conform to the specified standards of quality, environmental reliability laid down in our EMS on an ongoing basis.

We will ensure the operation of the proper managerial, technical and administrative controls, and related documentation, in order to enable this policy to be maintained at all levels. The management team will also ensure that a high level of customer satisfaction is maintained.

It is COMPANY's policy to ensure that all personnel involved in COMPANY's operations have appropriate training, so that each individual concerned understands the environmental aspects and controls of his/her responsibilities.

It is the responsibility of all COMPANY employees to support and apply those sections of the company environmental policy and procedures pertaining to their activities within the company. They must know how to initiate corrective actions on environmental matters, issues and concerns where and when appropriate.

In pursuance of this policy, COMPANY shall conform to the Environmental Management System specified by BS 7750 and the EU EMAS Regulation.

Our policy also embraces our relations with our suppliers, with whom we shall promote and implement continuous processes and procedures which are of mutual benefit and which also promote better environmental practices.

It is COMPANY policy to continually strive to improve environmental performance. See Environment Management Programme for our objectives and targets. Our environmental performance will be made publicly available, both at our premises and to the media as required. Our Environment Management Programme sets objectives and targets.

This policy is consistent also with general corporate policy, and at all times relates to our actual site and related indirect activities.

We, the management of COMPANY, commit to the environmental policy as described above.

____
General Manager — Date:__/__/__

____
Environmental Manager — Date:__/__/__

____
Manufacturing Manager — Date:__/__/__

____
Financial Controller — Date:__/__/__

____
Quality Assurance Manager — Date:__/__/__

____
Sales Administration Manager — Date:__/__/__

____
Human Resources Manager — Date:__/__/__

____
Documentation Manager — Date:__/__/__

____
Health and Safety Officer — Date:__/__/__

[*Note:* Original signatures are recorded on an Approvals Sheet – Ref. QD005.]

Environment organization chart, showing the responsibilities and reporting machanisms of an organization

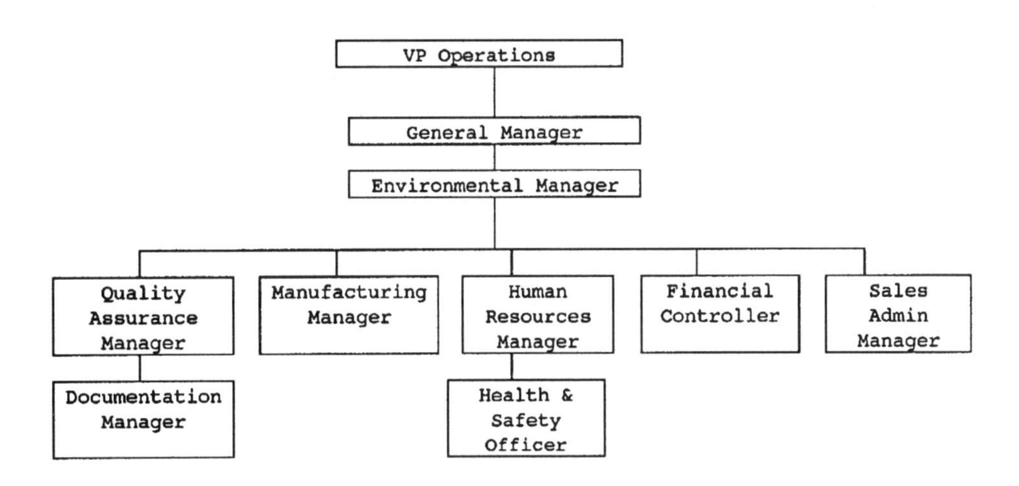

3.0 Organization and personnel (ISO 14001 clause 4.3)

3.1 Responsibility, authority and resources

The General Manager:
- has overall responsibility for the effect that the company has on the environment;
- is responsible for the implementation of corporate environmental polices;
- must ensure that the Environmental Management System and any other relevant quality systems are supported and maintained;
- has overall responsibility for the general welfare and safety of the workforce;
- must ensure that all purchases made by COMPANY are made with environmental policies in mind.

The Environment Manager
- is responsible for establishing, documenting and managing the Environmental Management System. This will be clearly documented and will include details of the control processes in the plant;
- reporting to the General Manager, has total authority for environmental management and the full backing of management for all actions he/she may deem necessary in carrying out his job;
- is responsible for ensuring that each department's responsibility for environmental issues is documented in an acceptable format and that adequate records are

maintained for demonstration of conformance to these requirements;
- must organize internal audits on the environmental system to ensure continued adherence to documented requirements;
- identifies, records and resolves, through designated channels, non-conformances within the environmental system;
- initiates action as needed and verifying that it has taken place;
- keeps abreast of relevant environmental legislative developments, issues and concerns;
- takes responsibility for communications, from/to outside and inside sources and destinations;
- takes immediate action where necessary on the receipt of communications needing such action.

The Manufacturing Manager is responsible for:
- ensuring that internal and third-party communications are accurate;
- ensuring that plant and equipment are maintained and controlled under the preventative maintenance system;
- Ref. EP-11;
- monitoring all maintenance schedules and emergency procedures with effect to environmental issues;
- controlling further activities until environmental deficiency has been corrected;
- taking whatever action is deemed appropriate in emergency situations.

The Financial Controller is responsible for:

- day-to-day control of all finances;
- preparation of budgets, short and long term planning;
- ensuring that funds are available to finance environmental related projects.

The Quality Manager is responsible for:

- managing and directing all quality resources to ensure that all material and products/services meet the required quality standards;
- monitoring vendor performance in the supply of goods and services, in terms of quality and environmental acceptability.

The Sales Administration Manager is responsible for:

- co-ordination of all order processing;
- replying to any sales related queries and ensuring that those concerning the environmental effect of our product/service are dealt with promptly.

The Human Resources Manager is responsible for:

- ensuring that all employees are adequately trained in the relevant quality and environmental issues;
- organization of manpower and the recruitment and selection of employees;

The Documentation Manager must:

- administer the documentation control system;
- control and co-ordinate the issue of engineering documentation to production;
- liaise with COMPANY in drafting functions on engineering drawing and specification issues;
- ensure that all environmental problems are recorded.

The Health and Safety Officer is responsible for:

- ensuring that the health and safety legislation as identified is implemented and monitored through periodic auditing;
- ensuring the health and safety at work of all employees;
- liaising with other management personnel in taking necessary action in an emergency situation.

The employees are responsible for:

- ensuring that all operations are carried out in accordance with the specified procedures and work practices;
- ensuring that safety equipment is used and instructions followed.

3.2 Verification resources and personnel

COMPANY has in its EMS laid down the verification requirements and procedures, and is committed to providing the resources and trained personnel for all necessary verification activities.

3.3 Management representative
The Environmental Manager will have responsibility for the implementation and maintenance of the Environmental Manuals, procedures, and relevant registers for BS 7750 and the EU EMAS regulation.

He/she will also have responsibility for all documentation in connection with the EMP and EMS.

The Environmental Management Review Team meet monthly to review progress of the system and programme.

3.4 Personnel, communication and training
(ISO 14001 clause 4.3.2)

COMPANY has a training programme to inform all personnel of the importance of complying with policy and objectives.

Personnel are made aware of the environmental benefits of effective job performance.

Personnel are made aware of the potential consequences of departure from agreed operating procedures.

All staff are made aware of their role and responsibilities in compliance with the policy.

The Environment Manager has the responsibility for communications, from/to outside and inside sources and destinations, and the authority to take immediate action where necessary on the receipt of communications needing such action. (ISO 14001 clause 4.3.3.)

COMPANY has implemented procedures to identify training needs.

COMPANY is maintaining records of training.

COMPANY shall ensure use of qualified personnel at all times in implementing these procedures.

Reference:	Quality Manual	-	QM-1, Section 4.20
	Training	-	QP-23
	Training Syllabus	-	TS-14
	Course	-	Booklet 5

4.0 Environmental effects (ISO 14001 clause 4.2.1)

4.1 Register of regulations

COMPANY has developed a Register of Regulations, which includes relevant laws, codes of practices and our policies on these and all related issues, pertaining to the environmental aspects of our activities, products and services. Our Environmental Management System ensures that we meet all the requirements of this register as a minimum objective.

Reference: Register of Regulations.

4.2 Communications

COMPANY has established and will maintain procedures for receiving, documenting and responding to communications, both internally and externally, from relevant interested parties concerning environmental effects and management. This also covers communication from the general public. All communications outside of those which are part of the EMS go to the Environment Manager in the first instance who decides if they signal a non-conformance needing action and, whether or not they do so, are considered and action decided on at the monthly environment management committee meetings.

Reference: Environment Management Programme.

4.3 Register of effects

COMPANY has established procedures for examining and assessing the environmental effects, both direct and indirect, of normal and abnormal operating procedures, incidents, accidents and potential emergency situations, in addition to current, past and planned activities, products or services and for compliance to the Register of Regulations. New developments are also monitored and controlled under the EMP procedure.

These procedures are contained in EMP, the Effects Evaluation Procedure, the Register of Effects and the Control and Monitoring Manual, and reflected also where necessary in the Health and Safety Manual and SOPs.

These records of environmental effects include all the actual or potential general environmental issues as they relate to our operations, and the specific issues involved in our operations.

Both of the above will relate to normal and abnormal operating conditions, to accidents, incidents, hazardous and risk situations.

In the first year, and for as long as it takes, these effects will also include the once-offs, or past occurrences identified in the PER, and controlled and cleaned up under the management of the monthly environment management committee meetings.

References: Register of Regulations - ERR-1
Register of Effects - ERE-1
Control and Monitoring Manual
Corrective Action - QP-2
Customer Returns - QP-24
PER

5.0 Objectives and targets

The objectives of the system are for COMPANY to operate as an environmentally-caring company and to demonstrate this by the employment of both ISO 14000/BS 7750 and ISO 9000 and (for EU companies) the EU EMAS Regulation. (See policy statement this manual, and the environment management programme.)

The main objectives are to operate and maintain manufacturing/service facility in a manner consistent with the best environmental practices, taking account of responsibilities to 'stakeholders'/parent company, customers, staff, suppliers and the community at large.

The general objectives are laid down in the policy statements in the Register of Regulations. The detailed objectives are in the Environment Management Programme. The current target is to meet the objectives laid down in the Environment Management Programme, by maintaining our environmental management system, relevant to all levels of our organization, certified to ISO 14000/BS 7750, and meeting the requirements of the EU EMAS Regulation.

Once this first objective is in place a new objective will be set, which will be to operate as far as possible a system of continuous environmental management improvement.

6.0 Management programme

6.1 The EMP
COMPANY has established and will maintain a programme for achieving the objectives and targets laid down, in accordance with ISO 14000/BS 7750 and the EU EMAS regulation. This is set up in detail in the EMP. Separate programmes and targets shall be developed in respect of the environmental management of projects relating to new developments.

Initial and on-going programme to include:
- designation of responsibility for targets at each level;
- means by which they are to be achieved.

Programmes for new developments shall include details of the following:
- details of environmental objectives to be obtained;
- mechanisms for their achievement;
- procedures for dealing with proposed changes;
- corrective mechanisms.

All significant issues and their effects are identified and controlled in the EMP and related procedures and documents. (ISO 14001 clause 4.3.6.)

6.2 Emergency response (ISO 14001 clause 4.3.7)
Emergency preparedness and response is managed and documented under the health and safety system, as per the Health

and Safety Manual and related documents. Management summaries are in the manual, while SOP 1 deals with emergency response procedures.

7.0 Environmental management manual and documentation
(ISO 14001 clause 4.3.4)

The requirements of the standard for documentation are met in this documented Environmental Management Manual and related documentation. The Environmental Management Manual and the Health and Safety Manual also contain abnormal and emergency activities.

These manuals and procedures outline controls which ensure that the plant operates within the required environmental regulations and requirements. Obsolete documents shall be removed with new relevant documentation available at all locations where operations essential to the effective functioning of the system are performed. Documents are controlled such that they can be identified, reviewed, revised and approved by authorized personnel. (ISO 14001 clause 4.3.5.)

The procedures will provide for the early and prompt detection of trends or conditions which could result in environmental damage and allow for effective corrective action to be taken.

Each system procedure will provide specific details on the execution of the pertinent functions.

Reference:	Register of Regulations	-	ERR-1
	Register of Effects		ERE-1
	Environment Procedures	-	EM-1 to EM-9
	Quality Manual	-	QM-1
	Health and Safety	-	S-1

8.0 Operational control (ISO 14001 clause 4.4)

8.1 General
Management responsibilities within COMPANY are clearly defined to ensure that control, verification and measurement are adequately co-ordinated and effectively performed.

This is achieved through the identification of the relevant issues in the Register of Effects and their control in the SOPs and the Control and Monitoring Manual.

Reference: Control and Monitoring Manual - CMM-1
Register of Effects
SOPs

8.2 Control
Through the above mechanisms COMPANY has identified the functions, activities and processes which affect, or have the potential to affect, the environment. Between the EMP and the EMS these are monitored, controlled and subjected to plans.

These mechanisms include SOPs, procurement measures, monitoring and control of processes, approvals and conformance criteria, supported by standards, codes of practice, legislation and/or licences.

8.3 Verification, measurement and testing
COMPANY has established and will maintain procedures for the verification of compliance with the levels in the

Environmental Management Programme, the Register of Effects and the Control and Monitoring Manual.

For each relevant activity or area, COMPANY has implemented measures to meet the identification, documentation, acceptance criteria, verification methods, non-conformance responses, and assessment and correction of systems required by the standard.

All monitoring and testing equipment is controlled and calibrated under our equipment testing and calibration procedures. (ISO 14001 clause 4.4.1.)

8.4 Non-conformances and corrective action
(ISO 14001 clause 4.4.2.)

All communication and/or complaints in relation to environmental issues, from whatever source, will be forwarded to the Environmental Manager. These will be dealt with as stated in the quality procedures as follows:

- the identification of cause;
- the initiation of a plan of action;
- the setting up of preventative measures;
- new/adapted controls;
- changes in procedures and their documentation as necessary.

Reference:	Quality Manual	– QM-1
	Non-conforming Product	– QP-1
	Corrective Action	– QP-2
	Customer Returns	– QP-24

9.0 Environmental records (ISO 14001 clause 4.4.3)

COMPANY has established and will maintain a system of records in order to demonstrate compliance with the requirements of the environmental management system, and to record the extent to which planned environmental objectives and targets have been met. These records shall be legible, retrievable and protected against potential damage. A policy as to their availability to interested parties both within and without the organization shall also be established.

The EMP and the documentation of the EMS are intended to meet the requirements of the standards in this respect, and these include records of procurement activities and training.

Reference: Quality Manual - QM-1, Section 4.15
Quality Records - QP-22
Environment Management Programme

Records and procedures are in place for both internal and external communications (ISO 14001 clause 4.3.3).

10.0 Audits (ISO 14001 clause 4.4.4)

10.1 General

COMPANY has established and will maintain audit procedures using as a guide the ISO 10000 series of standards. These will include an audit plan, which will check:

- whether our EMS activities are conforming to the requirements of the EMP;
- whether our systems are effective, both properly implemented and maintained;
- allow proper determination of the adequacy of the systems by management.

As they become available, the ISO 14010 series of environmental auditing standards will be used to adapt the ISO 10000 standards as necessary.

10.2 The audit plan/procedure

This will include:

The areas to be audited

- the organizational structure;
- administrative and operational procedures;
- the workplace, layout, operations;
- how well the EMS meets the requirements of the EMP.

Frequency of audits

- ranking of issues by priority/frequency;
- ranking by previous performance/non-conformance.

Who is responsible for auditing each area

The audit team
- independence of auditors;
- their relevant expertise;
- support from internal/external specialists.

The protocol of the audit (some or all of the following)
- questionnaires;
- interviews;
- direct observations;
- checklists (such as the pre-certification checklist);
- measurements.

Audit reports
- scope;
- level of conformity/non-conformity;
- effectiveness of EMS;
- implementation of corrective action;
- effectiveness of corrective action;
- conclusions and recommendations.

Procedures for publishing audit findings
- management/staff;
- interested outside parties.

Reference: Quality Manual – QM-1, Section 4.16
Internal Audits – QP-30.

11.0 Management review (ISO 14001 clause 4.5)

COMPANY's management does, at appropriate intervals, review the environmental management system adopted to satisfy the requirements of ISO 14000/BS 7750, to ensure its continuing suitability and effectiveness. Results, including those of environmental management audits, shall be published if required.

The reviews will establish the need if any to change policy, procedures, controls, objectives or other relevant matters, taking account of audit results, changing circumstances, including legislation and emerging codes of practice and our need for continual improvement.

Reference: Quality Manual – QM-1, Section 4.1.3
Management Review – QP-36.

12.0 Suppliers

It is the company's policy to relay any relevant information concerning environmental matters to our suppliers. We will assist our suppliers in the establishment of their environmental management system, which satisfies our requirements. This may vary from verbal/written communication to the undertaking of an environmental audit at their facility.

As the environmental criteria from our suppliers emerges this will be monitored under the procurement measures of our ISO 9000 system.

Reference: Annexe 1

Annexe 1 Vendor communication

Dear Sir/Madam,

We have implemented an environmental management system to the requirements of the Responsible Care Programme, ISO 14000/BS 7750, and the EU EMAS Regulation.

As with ISO 9000, this calls for vendor involvement, and in particular vendor audits of the environmental quality of components and services. We need to involve you with us in this respect, in what will be a confidential process. Our co-operation will need to be in the form of a Vendor Audit, in which we will need information concerning how well your products and services conform to environmental requirements, where these exist in the first instance in the form of directives or regulations and, where no such regulations exist, your policies on environmental concerns.

We may be able to do our audit from your existing evidence of compliance, or we may have to carry out an actual audit. The information you give us in reply to this letter, and the attached questionnaire, will be a great help in this respect. [See IER for these.]

Please regard this as a mutually beneficial project through which you also may attain these prestigious environmental standards. ISO 14000/BS 7750 is another ISO 9000 type standard, and the holders of the EU EMAS Regulation will be able both to display a prestigious logo and become listed in a special EU environmental honours list, so perhaps we can all do this together. We will certainly be happy to help.

Looking forward to hearing from you,

Regards,

Annexe 2 Environmental management programme

This EMP is contained in [give own company reference to EMP].

Annexe 3 Preparatory environmental review (IER)

The IER is contained in [give own company reference to IER].

Annexe 4 Links with ISO 9000

Many of the demands of ISO 14000/BS 7750 can be met under ISO 9000 and, as we have shown, both CEFIC and the CIA recommend an expanded ISO 9001 to embrace both quality and environmental requirements.

Here is a list of the procedures for BS 7750 which can be controlled under ISO 9000. What is meant by this is that you simply expand the columns in your ISO 9000 system to cater for environmental issues.

These are adapted from the table in Annexe B of BS 7750

Contract review
Design control
Documentation control
Purchasing
Inspection and testing
Calibration of equipment

Non-conforming procedures
Corrective action
Handling, storage, packaging and delivery
Internal audits
Training

The table gives several more which the reader should study, however, the author has found the elements in the above list easy to apply under ISO 9000, while some of the others listed appeared to us to fit more easily into the environmental management system.

Appendix 3

Overhead Transparencies for Management Presentation

In the following pages samples of overhead transparencies are shown. These are used in briefing management and in presentations to interested organizations.

The samples are, of course, necessarily selective and companies who use these pages of the book will no doubt want to adapt them or substitute their own versions.

Overhead #1

THE STATUS OF BS 7750

BS 7750

- Final edition was published in 1994

Other national versions

- There are some national versions such as the French X 30 200 and Irish IS 310

ISO 14000

- Committees currently sitting. Draft contents now known. May be ready 1996. Not expected to differ from BS 7750.

Companies worldwide are starting to adopt BS 7750 in anticipation of it being the ISO model.

The EU is already saying that BS 7750 meets the EMAS regulation.

US interest in BS 7750 is fuelled by its interest in EMAS.

Lawyers are showing an interest in the relevance of ISO 14000/BS 7750.

Overhead #2

Elements which can be covered

Traditional environmental

Staff health and safety

Product/service safety/integrity

Public safety

Overhead #3

The general issues

Physical planning

Environmental impact assessment

Air emissions

Effluent discharges

Water supplies and sewage treatment

Waste - normal and toxic

Packaging

Nuisances

Noise

Radiation

Amenities, trees and wildlife

Urban renewal/site dereliction

Safety/security of service/product

Materials and energy usage

Public safety

Staff health and safety

Overhead #4

The specific issues

All the general issues of relevance

Site specific issues

Operational/service specific issues

Supplier issues

Overhead #5

Packaging issues

Over-packaging

Redundancy

Biodegradability

Toxicity

Reusability

Recyclability

Retrievability

Alternate use after delivery

Overhead #6

The project/procedure

Legal issue questionnaire to establish legislation

Preliminary Environmental Review (PER or IER))

The Register of Regulations

Environment Management Programme

Environment Management System

EMS documentation

Pre-certification check

Training

Certification

Overhead #7

Attractions for company

Legal implications

- both corporate and personal for management
- environmental regulations
- staff health and safety
- public safety
- operational integrity/safety

A third-party certified best code of practice, in the event of accidents and/or unjustified claims of negligence

PR and marketing/other

Staff morale working for a best practice company

Interest in being an accredited best practice company

Being the first company in our group

Potential cost savings through waste/resource optimization

Overhead #8

Potential direct benefits

Reduction in resource consumption

Raw materials

Energy

Reduction in scrap or waste

Reduction in complaints and follow-up

Avoidance of accidents or emergencies

Avoidance of claims

Avoidance of fines and penalties

Avoidance of personal liability

Overhead #9

Potential indirect benefits

Enhanced corporate image

Enhanced marketing capabilities

Improved staff morale

Better customer relations

Better community relations

Overhead #10

Key elements to be addressed

Policy, management and documentation

Is there a clearly defined environment policy?

Is there a management system for executing the policy?

Is the management system clearly documented?

Is there a document control system?

Have responsibilities and authority been stated?

Is there a training and education programme?

Overhead #11

More key elements

Are there clearly defined procedures?

Is there a register of issues?

Is there an environment management manual?

Is there a Register of Regulations?

Are the results of monitoring being recorded and presented to management?

Are there targets and objectives?

Overhead #12

The main documented steps

Initial plan

Project plan

Preparatory review (called preliminary, or initial, environmental review or PER)

Inventory of regulations (called Register of Regulations)

Inventory of environmental effects (called Register of Environmental Effects)

The Environment Management Manual

The Environment Management Programme/System

Training

Pre-registration audit

Application for certification

Overhead #13

List of overall potential effects

Planning

Effluent discharge

Solid and toxic waste

Use of harmful substances
- radioactive sources
- pesticides
- chemicals

Product disposal

Safe drinking water

Use of water

Materials minimization (in house)

Energy conservation

Emergency control/health and safety

Supplier management

Appendix 4

Pre-certification Checklists

This pre-certification inspection checklist for ISO 9000 is based on one kindly supplied by SGS Yarsley UK.

The checklist is for documentation only. It precedes and supplements the shop floor internal inspection which makes sure that what the documentation tells us is really in place.

Documentation Questionnaire

9001 Requirement

4.1.1 QUALITY POLICY
Documented and acceptable

4.1.2 ORGANIZATION
All responsibilities and authorities clearly defined

4.1.2 Verification resources identified and adequate

4.1.2 Management representative appointed

4.1.3 Quality System reviewed at appropriate intervals and recorded

4.3 CONTRACT REVIEW

Procedures ensure that:
Contract requirements documented
Differences from tender resolved
Supplier has capability to meet contractual requirements

4.4 DESIGN CONTROL

Procedure covers:

4.4.2 Design and Development Planning including updating procedures

4.4.3 Design input requirements - Procedure for identifying inputs

4.4.4 Design output - adequate procedures

4.4.5 Design verification procedures

4.4.6 Design changes - procedure for review and approval

4.5 DOCUMENT CONTROL

Procedures for approval and issue, changes and modifications

4.6 PURCHASING

4.6.2 Procedures for control of:
Suppliers
Sub-contractors

4.6.3 Procedure ensures purchasing data is adequate

4.6.4 Purchaser afforded right to verify at source?

4.7 PURCHASER SUPPLIED PRODUCT

Procedures for verification, storage and maintenance

4.8 PRODUCT IDENTIFICATION AND TRACEABILITY

Identification at all stages
Traceability procedures to the extent required

4.9 PROCESS CONTROL

4.9.1 Procedures show that production and installation processes are identified and planned

4.9.1 Work instructions documented

4.9.1 Procedures ensure use of suitable production and installation equipment, working environment and compliance with reference standards codes and quality plans

4.9.1 Procedure includes monitoring and control of process and product characteristics

4.9.1 Criteria for workmanship stipulated. Control of workmanship standards documented

4.9.2 Control of special processes documented including: qualification of processes and records

4.10 INSPECTION AND TESTING

4.10.1 RECEIVING INSPECTION AND TESTING

Procedures include:
verification prior to release
recall procedures
records

4.10.2 IN PROCESS INSPECTION AND TESTING

Procedures include:

- adequate inspection and testing of product, quality plans, etc
- establishing product conformance by monitoring and controls
- hold procedures including release/recall procedures
- identification of non-conforming product

4.10.3 FINAL INSPECTION AND TESTING

Procedures ensure that all previous inspections and tests have been conducted and data meets specified requirements

Procedure describes final inspection and testing to be carried out or reference to Quality plans

Procedures ensure product is not despatched until all final activities have been completed and associated data documentation is available and authorized

4.10.4 INSPECTION AND TEST RECORDS

Procedures for maintaining records that product has passed inspection/tests with defined acceptance criteria

4.11 INSPECTION, MEASURING AND TEST EQUIPMENT

Procedure includes:

- selection of appropriate equipment

- identifying, calibrating, adjusting equipment at prescribed intervals against national standards

- calibration procedures, details of equipment type, identification number, location, frequency of checks, methods, acceptance criteria and action to be taken when results are unsatisfactory

- ensuring that equipment is capable of accuracy and precision necessary

- identification of equipment calibration status (labelling etc)

- records of equipment

- assessment of previous inspection results when equipment is found to be out of calibration

- suitable environmental conditions for calibrations, etc

- handling, preservation and storage of equipment

- safe-guarding of inspection, measuring and test facilities, including hardware and software from adjustment which would invalidate settings

- checking of test hardware (e.g. jigs, fixtures, templates, patterns) and test software when used as suitable forms of inspections at prescribed intervals including records

4.12 INSPECTION AND TEST STATUS

Inspection and test status identified by suitable means throughout production and installation, ensuring that only 'passed' product is despatched, used or installed

4.13 CONTROL OF NON-CONFORMING PRODUCT

Procedures cover:
- identification, documentation, evaluation, segregating (when practical) and disposition

4.14 CORRECTIVE ACTION

Procedures for:

- investigating cause and corrective action needed

- analysis of processes, work operations, concessions, records, service, reports, customer complaints

- initiating corrective action

- controls to ensure corrective action is taken and is effective

- implementing and recording changes resulting from corrective action

4.15 HANDLING, STORAGE, PACKAGING AND DELIVERY

4.15.2 Procedure for methods and means of handling

4.15.3 Procedure for storage authorized issues and receipt from store, checks of product in stock for conditions

4.15.4 Requirements for packing, preservation and marking defined including materials used

4.15.5 Procedure for protection of product quality after final inspection and test (including delivery to customer if contractually required)

4.16 QUALITY RECORDS

Procedures for: identifying, collecting, indexing, filing, storage, maintenance and disposition of records

Records demonstrate achievement of required quality and effective operation of the quality system

Records to be stored and retrievable in suitable facilities and environment

Retention times specified

4.17 INTERNAL QUALITY AUDITS

Procedures for planned and documented quality audits, including audit schedule, audit and follow-up procedures, distribution of results, timely corrective action

4.18 TRAINING

Procedure for: identifying and providing training needs for all personnel performing activities affecting quality

Personnel qualified and records maintained

4.19 SERVICES

Procedure where specified in the contract

4.20 STATISTICAL TECHNIQUES
Procedures where appropriate

Pre-certification inspection checklist for BS 7750

This checklist was kindly supplied by SGS Yarsley UK.

This checklist is for documentation only. It precedes and supplements the shop floor internal inspection which makes sure that what the documentation tells us is really in place.

Ref No Requirement
BS 7750

Documentation Questionnaire

BS 7750 - Environmental Management System

PREPARATORY ENVIRONMENTAL REVIEW

1) Was a PER performed

2) Did PER cover
a) legislative and regulatory requirements

b) evaluation and registration of significant environmental effects

c) examination of existing environmental management practices

d) assessment of feedback from investigation of incidents

3) To what extent was PER used in the development of the system

a) considerably

b) moderately

c) slightly or not at all

4) Comment on the quality and applicability of the conclusions of the PER

4.1 ENVIRONMENTAL MANAGEMENT SYSTEM

Documented and acceptable
Takes account of claimed Codes of Practice

4.2 ENVIRONMENTAL POLICY

a) Relevant to activities, products, services and their environmental effects
b) Understood, maintained and implemented at all levels
c) Publicly available
d) Commitment to continual improvement
e) Allows for setting and publication of environmental objectives

4.3 ORGANIZATION AND PERSONNEL

4.3.1 RESPONSIBILITY, AUTHORITY AND RESOURCES

All responsibilities and authorities clearly defined
Sufficient resources and personnel
Action is initiated to ensure compliance with policy
Environmental problems are identified and recorded
Solutions are initiated, recommended or provided through designed channels
Implementation of solutions verified
Control further activities until deficiency corrected
Act in the emergency situation

4.3.2 VERIFICATION RESOURCES AND PERSONNEL

Organization defines in-house verification requirements
Organization provides adequate resources and trained personnel for verification

4.3.3 MANAGEMENT REPRESENTATIVE

Management representative appointed with defined authority

4.3.4 PERSONNEL COMMUNICATION AND TRAINING

Personnel made aware of:-

- Importance of compliance with policy and objectives
- environmental benefits of effective job performance
- potential consequences of departure from agreed operating procedures
- their role and responsibilities in compliance with the policy

Organization has procedures to:-

- identify training needs
- maintain records of training
- ensure use of qualified personnel

4.4 ENVIRONMENTAL EFFECTS

4.4.1 REGISTER OF LEGISLATIVE, REGULATORY AND OTHER POLICY REQUIREMENTS

Procedures for recording legislative, regulatory and policy requirements

4.4.2 COMMUNICATIONS

Procedures for receiving, documenting and responding to relevant communication

4.4.3 ENVIRONMENTAL EFFECTS EVALUATION AND REGISTER

Records of environmental effects to include, where appropriate

a) all emissions to atmosphere
b) all discharge to water
c) waste
d) contamination of land
e) use of all natural resources (incl. land, water fuels, energy)
f) noise, odour, dust, vibration and visual impact
g) effects on eco-system and specific parts of environment

Procedures to record those effects arising from:-

1) normal operations
2) abnormal operating procedures
3) incidents, accidents and potential emergency situations
4) past activities, current activities and planned activities

4.5 ENVIRONMENTAL OBJECTIVES AND TARGETS

Objectives and targets consistent with policy
Commitment to continual improvement in appropriate areas
Procedure to specify objectives and targets to all relevant levels in organization

4.6 ENVIRONMENTAL MANAGEMENT PROGRAMME

Programme to include:-

a) designation of responsibility for targets at each level
b) means by which they are achieved

Separate programmes in respect of projects to include:-

c) environmental objectives to be obtained
d) mechanisms for their achievement
e) procedures for dealing with change
f) corrective mechanisms

4.7 ENVIRONMENTAL MANAGEMENT MANUAL AND DOCUMENTATION

4.7.1 MANUAL

a) collates the environmental policy, objectives, targets and programme
b) documents key roles and responsibilities
c) describes interaction of system elements
d) gives direction to related documentation
e) covers abnormal operating conditions incidents, accidents, emergencies

4.7.2 DOCUMENTATION

Documents are controlled such that:-

a) they can be identified
b) they are reviewed, revised and approved by authorized personnel
c) current versions are available at relevant locations
d) obsolete documents are promptly removed from point of issue or use

4.8 OPERATIONAL CONTROL

4.8.2 CONTROL

Identification of functions, activities, processes effecting environment

Controlled conditions to include:-

a) documented work instruction for own and other employees
b) procedures for procurement and contract activities
c) monitoring and control of relevant process characteristics (eg waste, effluent)
d) approval of planned processes and equipment
e) criteria for performance by written standards

4.8.3 VERIFICATION, MEASUREMENT AND TESTING

a) necessary verification information is identified and documented
b) necessary verification procedures are specified and documented
c) acceptance criteria and necessary action are established and documented

d) previous verification information is assessed when verification system malfunctioning

4.8.4 NON-COMPLIANCE AND CORRECTIVE ACTION

Responsibility and Authority defined for corrective action

In event of non-compliance, Management Representative and Manager shall:-

a) determine cause
b) draw up action plan
c) initiate preventive action
d) apply control, to ensure effective preventive actions
e) record changes in procedures resulting from corrective action

4.9 ENVIRONMENTAL MANAGEMENT RECORDS

Procedures with respect to records for:-

Identification
Collection
Indexing
Filing
Storage
Maintenance
Disposition

Records should be:-

Retrievable
Protected
Legible

Policy on availability of records

4.10 ENVIRONMENTAL MANAGEMENT AUDITS

4.10.1 GENERAL

Does Audit plan set out to determine:-

(i) If activities conform to environmental programme
(ii) If activities are implemented effectively
(iii) Effectiveness of system in fulfilling policy

4.10.2 AUDIT PLAN

Does plan cover:-

a) specific activities/area including:-

1) organization structure
2) administrative and operational procedures
3) work areas operations and processes
4) documentation reports and records
5) environmental performance

b) frequency of auditing of each activity/area
c) responsibility for auditing each activity/area
d) personnel requirement. Are auditors:-

1) independent of the specific activity/area audited
2) in possession of relevant expertise of the activity/area
3) in possession of support from specialists

e) protocol for conducting audits includes:-

1) interviews
2) checklists
3) questionnaires
4) measurements
5) observations

f) procedures for reporting audit findings. Reports should address:-

1) conformity level of system elements with requirements

2) effectiveness of system in meeting objectives/targets
3) implementation of corrective action
4) conclusions and recommendations

g) procedures for publishing audit findings

4.11 ENVIRONMENTAL MANAGEMENT REVIEWS

Are there reviews?
Are reviews published?
Do reviews include results of environmental management audits?

Index